C000097670

NORTHERN MINING ROOTS

By

BERNARD McCORMICK

I would like to thank Alistair Bowden and Jean Gartland from the Coleport Library, Durham City which is a department of the Culture & Leisure section of Durham County Council. For guiding me to the brilliant Coal Mining Site: and their permission for reproducing the Colliery Photograph's. My book is mainly aimed at the older miner who does not use a computer and therefore will not be able to have access to this brilliant Durham County Council Cultural section Coal Mining site: also Jullian Harrops Assistant head at Beamish Photographic Archive for kindly giving permission for five of the Photograph's owned by Beamish Archives

First Published in England in the United Kingdom
In the year 2005
By Bermac Publications, Aycliffe,
www.bermac.co.uk
E/Mail books@bermac.co.uk
Tel. 01325-311956

ISBN 0-9541756-7-0

Typeset in Times New Roman
Titles in Tiffany HV BT
Typesetting and originating by
Bermac Publications.
Printed and Bound in Great Britain
BY MACDONALD PRESS LIMITED, TUDHOE.

FOREWORD

I n the years starting 1700 in the North of England there was great changes in our way of life. The Wealth of the Country at this time was coal. This precious commodity from the Strata below us was the source of growth & prosperity that we were depending on to pay our way in the World. Rich men from the South of England with rich landowners within the region took advantage of the tremendous demand for coal and its by-products to make vast profits. They exploited their land as well as hard working miners from the Northern areas of the Country.

In my book 'Northern Mining Roots', I have completed an A to Z History of the ownership of Collieries, sinking dates and a wealth of other information on the Industry that our forefathers relied on for a meagre living in days gone by. The History also includes photographs of many of our most important Collieries. I have used most of the Mining photograph's from the 'Durham Miner Project', operated throughout County Durham and part of Sunderland. They received help and funding from Durham,CC, and most other organisations like the European Social Fund and North East Museums. They had a Database, Many Colliery Histories and also mapping. The only problem was not all of my generation who worked in mining had access to Computers. I decided to make a lot of the photograph's available to these people in this book. I was very grateful to Mr. Alistair Bowden who works in a Government Department and he advised me on the site and the procedure for applying for permission to use the photographs. The book further includes an analysis of the types of coal that we worked on a daily basis the sizes of the particular seams and many of the most difficult sinking while I do appreciate there are many more Collieries than I have recordered; I have noted as many as I possibly could in this small publication.

In the third Chapter I have provided an insight in the difficult period when the Industry was in its early stages. The fight by our ancestors to make a meagre living. It also tells the story of the early fight by the Miners to establish Trade Unions with men to put over their point of view to the Manipulative Coal owners and speculators that used scab workers from other parts of the Country. Paid bullies and Bailiffs turned families out of their homes; and the tremendous fight back to gain recognition. I have also included a brief synopsis of leading leaders in the Industry; people for instance Doctor Wilson, William Hammond Patterson and Tommy Ramsey.

In the final Chapter I have told the story of Ken Robinson from Witton Park. Who was just an ordinary Northern Miner who loved the Coal Industry. The whole of his family worked as miners; the book tells of their early family struggles and fight for life, during the many problems in the Mining Industry at 'Witton Park',. During the downturn of the Industry in the fifties Ken took his whole family to Shropshire to continue working in the pits which he loved so much. Ken very much supported the Miners in their final fight against the Thatcher Government; there was never one week when he did not send a contribution or offer encouragement in this hard and testing time for the miners. Ken qualified as a Deputy then as an inspector I have followed his career to the present. He is now 79 and retired from work but has one of the greatest collections of books on Mining and Industry in the North/ East; as well as many artefacts, lamps and other memorabilia from the coal industry. His son is a Head of the European History Department of a Los Angelus High School living in Los Angelus, America. Ray informed me that he is now an 'American Citizen' & married to his Chinese wife in the 'City of Angels'; but his heart is still in North East England. Kens daughter is a very respected Union Representative for the 'Transport & General Union'. All of the family have travelled for years to our Durham Gala and are proud of their connection to the area.

3

Cover   Young Miners from Elemore Collieries

Young Miners from the East Hetton (Kelloe) waiting to descend the pit; the camaraderie was amazing among the lads who allowed themselves one cigarette before going down. Most chewed backy down the pit to help in getting rid of the coal dust. Smoking in the Pit was forbidden and it was compulsory for everyone to carry a testing lamp when getting out of the cage at their particular seam they would be searched for contraband and also that their lamps were properly locked. Most of the lads would be employed as drivers, putters or timber leaders and most put down their own weigh for the tubs and trolleys to run on; life was extremely hard for them in every way but there was never complaints; they just got on with the job.

Dates of Sinking of North Eastern Pit Shafts

A *great part of the success and wealth of our Country were the reserves of coal in the strata below our Country. To a great deal of our early ancestors, this was better than having reserves of gold below their feet. Currency from which made a hard earned living for them and their families. There were many scrupulous land owners who used their freehold as the start of coal producing Collieries. Many were in the business just to get rich rewards; other coal mine owners were fair in their employment of people. The following is an A to Z list of the Collieries; I have endeavoured to get the information as accurate as possible:*

Addison

The Stella Coal Company, was sunk in 1864, the shaft was linked to Starsgate, Greenside, Clara Vale, and the Emma pit at Ryton. Men working in 1930 was 475, by 1950, 386, and by 1960 was 145, the Colliery closed in February, 1963:

Adelaide (Shildon Bank Top)

This was the Jane Pit, owned by Joseph Pease & Partners, from 1830 to1889, the coal was drawn from the Busty, and the Harvey, it was later owned by the West Durham Wallsend Coal Company.

Adventure

After work ceased on the sinking of the shaft in 1815, because of excessive water, it was restarted in 1821-2, the first coals coming from the Hutton Seam, in 1823, later in 1870; coal was produced from the Low Main. The Londonderry Family owned the pit, and they carried on working the pit until, 1896. In 1912-13, Messrs. Cooks worked the Colliery, by the system of Board and Pillar, as a Drift Mine, in 1916. By 1930, it was owned by, The Rainton Coal Company Limited. Arc-wall cutting was employed, in 1951. The Maudlin was worked out in 1959, when Main and Low Main coal was worked, but the pit was plagued by water problems and finally closed on the 21 July 1978, after many years of producing coal.

Allerdene

Mining has gone on in this pit since the very early days, even prior to 1700. The pit was in use with a pumping engine, in 1844, this together with Betty and Street Pits, made up the Team Colliery. Messrs. Perkins

Adventure Colliery

Auckland Park Colliery

Annefield Plane above

Below last shift at Ashington Colliery

Annefield Plane Colliery below Shift End at a Typical Colliery

& Partners, later called 'Pelaw Main Coal Company', owned the pit. The yard seam was abandoned in 1930, the Low Main also in 1938, and the pit finally closed in 1962.

Andrews House

Mining was undertaken in a small way at Andrews House Farm, and also Fortune Hill, both pits closing in 1856. John Bowes sunk the main Pit, in 1843, which was south of Marley Hill Colliery, the pit finally closing in 1931.

Auckland Park

This pit was formerly called Black Boy Colliery. It was re-named by Bolckow, Vaughan & Company, who worked it in the years 1856-1897. It was made up of 2 shafts, north & south. The Harvey and Brockwell, was worked, in the 1890s, the coal was washed on site, and coke was produced in Beehive ovens, for metallurgical use. Dorman and Long took over the pit in 1929. In 1930, 47 men were employed, in 1940, 318 were employed. The pit finally closed in 1948.

Beamish

This pit dated from 1763, first sunk by Morton Davidson; in 1849, Beamish Air Pit was sunk. The Mary pit was sunk in 1883, by James Joicey, also sinking the James Pit in 1885, Joicey also worked the Beamish no. 2, and also the Busty in the 1880s. In 1911 work ceased at the Hutton, Shield Row, and the James Pit, the Brockwell ceased in 1926, and all three restarted in 1929. Further north from these the Copy shaft was sunk in 1942. The Mary Pit being the main coal drawing shaft, at that time, Major improvements were carried out in 1951, when skip loading was started, in 1954-5. The pit finally closed in March 1966.

Bearpark

The Bearpark Coal Co. sunk Bearpark Brancepeth Colliery, in 1872, and the first seam worked was the Hutton, followed by a shaft to the Brockwell, in 1874, Coke from Beehive ovens began in 1877. Simon Carves retort ovens later replaced these. The washer unit closed in 1961, and the coal from the Victoria coal was sent to the Morrison Busty wash, the Tilley using the facilities of Brandon Pit House. Skip loading started in 1962, and in 1983 with 500 men produced 152,000 tons of coal from the Tilley and Harvey which were thin seams, Multi- gib cutter loaders were used. The pit closed 6th. April 1984.

Bewick Main

Mining started as early as 1809, with a self-acting incline, Perkins and Partners, who operated Birtley Iron Works, and also the Ouston group of Collieries, Ravensworth and Urpeth, sank a later shaft. The name of the Company changed in 1906, to the owners of the Pelaw Main Collieries Ltd., and in 1926, to Pelaw Main Collieries, Limited. At Bewick Main, the Six

Beamish Colliery

below Bedlington

Quarter was worked out in 1931, and the Low Main and the Hutton, in 1932, the pit finally closed in 1933.

Binchester

The West Hartlepool Harbour and Rail Company sank Binchester in 1872, then it was taken over by Hunwick and Newfield Coal Company, Bolckow, Vaughan and Co. then purchased it in the 1880s. The pit was linked to Westerton. The Harvey and Brockwell was worked in 1890, and a new ventilating shaft was sunk in 1906 at Merrington Lane, the pit finally closed in 1908. The Vinovia shaft is now used for pumping water.

Black Boy

Mining started here in 1830, when Nicholas Wood and Co owned it. In 1850, it was worked under the name of Black Boy Coal Company, and there were three pits under this title, Old Black Boy Colliery, North of Auckland Park, The Machine Pit, to the south, and the Gurney near Coundon Grange. In 1860 these pits were recorded as being owned by the executors of J. Backhouse. Later Balckow and Vaughan acquired them, in 1884. The machine pit was re-named Auckland Park Colliery. In 1890 the Main and Five Quarter were worked, the pit finally closing December 1924, re-started again but again closed, in 1928. In 1929, it was owned by Dorman and Long, finally closing in 1939.

Blackhall

Hordon Collieries Ltd. owned the lease, in 1901. An up cast and downcast was sunk in October, through water bearing Strata, and by 1913 they were completed. Board and Pillar was worked from the Hutton and Low Main, and long wall working was introduced in 1947. Skip loading was introduced in 1956, and power loading was introduced, incorporating an Anderton sheerer in 1962, by then the Hutton Low Main and Hutton were being worked, with the most important customer being ICI. Water became a problem in 1979, over 2000 gallons a minute had to be pumped from the shaft pumps. Because of this problem shorter faces were worked, The Low Main was used to produce coals for Redcar Steel works. Because of water the pit closed on 16th. Of April 1981.

Black House

Black House, (H) was also known as the Wash House Pit, and was situated near Birtley, part of the Pelaw Main Colliery Group, together with Urpeth©, Bewick Main (D), Ouston (E), and also the Ravensworth Betty and Shop Pits. The pit opened in 1913, and in 1930 was owned by a French Company. The pit closed in 1932.

Black Prince

Situated near Dan's Castle, Tow Law, was sunk in 1846, by Charles Attwood, who started the Weardale Iron Company. The pit was near to the

LEASINGTHORN   below Binchester

Beamish Twizzell

below Burnhope

The Colliery, Bewicke Main.

Bewick Main

below Blackhall Colliery

Blackhall Colliery.

Royal George Pit, and had many coke ovens as part of the set-up. The Ballerat was worked in 1890, with approx. 630 workers, Five Quarter, Top, and also the Main Coal was also worked. In 1858-1921, the Victoria Pit, was worked at Tow Law fell, this was linked to the main pit by tramway. In 1906 a new drift was opened, for the Five Quarter coal, connected to this was a new Hauler and Washer. The pit finally closed in 1933.

Blaydon Main

Operated as a mine since the 17th. Century, G. H. Ramsey, owned it until 1884, when it was purchased by, Stella Coal Company, who worked 3 pits, The Hazard, Mary, and Speculation pits. Priestman Collier's limited bought them in 1908. Coke ovens were part of the operation at Derwenthaugh; the pit was finally closed in 1921.

Bolden

The Harton Coal Company sank the pit, in 1866-9. The no. 8 surface boiler killed two people in 1884. In 1890, The Bensham and Hutton seams were worked. In 1949 surface operations were modified, and Anderton, disk Shearer's was introduced to the pit, on Long Wall faces. In 1961, the pit employed 1240 men, but in February 1981, the National Coalboard announced its closure. The workmen made other test borings, after pressure to prolong the Colliery, but insufficient reserves were found, and the last shift at the pit was worked on 24th. Of June 1982.

Bowburn

I worked here, from leaving school, for the following 5 years, working, in the Hutton, on a Loader, then as a Hand Putter. The early owner of this pit was William Hedley, and later ownership was passed to West-Hartlepool Harbour and Railway Company, after this the Bell Bros., Colliery was sunk by the piling method, in 1906, by E. Johnson and sons, mainly to relieve the excessive haulage from Tursdale Colliery. Later Dorman and Long owned the pit, a new screening plant and washer was added to the pit in 1932. The coal from Tursdale was drawn through the goaf, by a drift, to the Bowburn shaft, in 1930, using the old shaft for ventilation, coal drawing and man riding. In 1930 639 men worked at the pit, rising to 2,358, in 1940, and 2,102, by 1960, finally closing in 1967.

Bowden Close

The Brockwell seam was found from test borings in 1839. Joseph Pease & Partners Ltd. worked the pit as Norwich Pit, and later as Pease & Partners Ltd. The pit closed in June 1930 with a loss of 1,200 jobs.

Brancepeth

The Northern Coal Mining Company sank the (A) pit at Brancepeth, around 1840, when Straker & Love, worked it. In 1855, the (B) pit at Oakenshaw, was also sunk, and the © pit in 1865. The major seams were The Hutton,

Bolden Colliery 1949

Donkins Row, Bolden 1960

BOWBURN

below **Burnhope**

Seggar, Jet, Three Quarter, Ballaratt, Harvey and Brockwell. There were 420 coke ovens on site, which rose to 1,700, in 1896. There was an explosion at the (A) pit on the 13th. Of April 1896, when, 20 men were killed. In 1902, 120 Semet Solvay, ovens were installed, after a by-product, recovery was made. In 1930 2,653 men were employed, 1960, 1,529, the pit closed in 1967.

Brandon

Originally owned and worked by John Shaw, in 1836. The (A) shaft was sunk in 1856 by Straker and Love, they also sank the (B) pit to the Busty, in 1860, and they also sank, the 'New Side', in 1884 to further the work in the Busty. After reserves were exhausted in the Brockwell and Busty, a new shaft was completed at Brandon Pit House, in 1924, with also a shaft at the Busty in 1931. The pit was modernised in 1927, with a new Heapstead, at the same time removing the beehive coke ovens. Eventually the © pit reserves declined, and pit house was developed, which had modern conveyors, in 1948-9. In 1957, a washer was constructed, and the conveyance of coal with a drift system, instead of the cage system. On 15th. Of March Pit-House finally closed.

Broomside

Known as The Lady Adelaide, Lord Londonderry sunk this pit to the Hutton in 1835, exporting the coal from Sunderland and Seaham. Broomside Coal Company, worked the pit, in the years, 1870-1880, and was finally worked out in 1890.

Browney

Bell Brothers sank this pit in 1871-73, having three shafts. The seams worked were Brockwell, Busty, and Hutton. The pit was taken over in 1923 by Dorman and Long, and in 1930, there was 625 employed. The pit finally closed, because of water problems in 1938.

Brussleton

Originally the pit was sunk in 1834, and another pit was sunk in 1897-1920, the Ladysmith Colliery, to the south of Banksandsides farm, later replaced these in 1939. Between 1920-1939 there was a new Brussleton Colliery, sunk further east. The Main Coal was worked via. Haggs Lane drift, in 1947 and the Beaumont seam was flooded in 1959. By 1967 the Harvey no. 1 had deteriorated in quality, and there was geological faults in the Busty, leaving the Harvey No. 2 as the only seam. The pit finally closed in 7th. June 1968.

Burnhope

Thomas Hedley Bros. Sank this pit in 1845, called the Fortune, or Sykes, pit. The Annie, Fell, and Jaw Blades, shafts were sunk in 1868, with the latter Jaw Blades, only lasting 3 years. For some years they were owned by

BROWNEY   below BRANCEPETH

NEW PIT BRANCEPETH COLLIERY.

Messrs Sowerby and Fletcher, and in 1881, they were acquired by, Utrick Ritson in 1881. He worked the Annie, Fell, Fortune, Rabbit Warren, and Ralph drifts, until 1934. Halmshaw and Partners then worked Burnhope, after this it then went into the ownership of Bearpark Coal and Coke Co. Ltd. With an Ariel flight to Bearpark Colliery, by 1942, Burnhope finally closing in 1949.

Burnhopefield (*Hobson*)
John Bowes and Partners Ltd. Operated this pit in 1849, when the Main and Busty, were worked, producing 140.000 tons of coal a year. In 1930 employing 394 men, 1940, 669, these figures were greatly reduced in 1960, until after the exhaustion of the Tilley, forced closure on 9th. August 1968.

Butterknowle
Two bronze Cauldrons were found in 1960, after breaking into old workings, with 2 repaired skillets. Which were dated from the 15th. Century. Both items are now in the Bowes Museum. In 1820-1830 William Prattman, worked the pit, but after having problems sinking a third shaft the Diamond he became bankrupt, and operations transferred to his trustees, after the market improved the Diamond pit was re-started. The Butterknowle Coal Company, in the 1880s also operated Marsfield drift, Quarry and Slacks pits, and also Moor Hill pits, up to 1885. A case was brought to Chancery High Court for damages for subsidence (Bishop Auckland Industrial Co-operative v The Butterknowle Colliery Company Ltd.) and this caused the pit to close in 1906.

Byermoor
The Clavering family carried out mining here in 18th. Century, by 1860, John Bowes and Partners Limited, ran operations. The Busty and Brockwell were the major seams, in 1890, and in 1938, the Brass Thill, was exhausted. The pit closed in 1968.

Byers Green
The Royalties were leased by The Durham County Coal Company, in 1840, the same year the Michael pit was sunk. There was trouble with water, but the shaft was still completed by 1845. Two more shafts were sunk in 1859 and 1873, after this it was taken over by The West Hartlepool Harbour & Railway Company, who sold it to Bolckow, Vaughan & Co. in 1877. The Busty & Brockwell were the main seams, in the 1990s. For a while it closed in 1927, but re-opened when amalgamating with Newfield. The pit finally closed in 1931.

Carterthorne
Henry Chaytor, of Witton Castle, operated this pit, in 1870, Hodgeson and Simpson taking over the interests in 1885. Carterthorne Colliery Owners,

BYERS GREEN COLLIERY | BYERS GREEN COKE OVENS

took over in 1886, later in 1891 Chaytor wanted to restart the Colliery, which was then leased on a lease from, The Earl of Strathmore, this being a yearly lease, for a total of 14 years, this was never executed. The case was heard in the High Court Chancery Dept; and the receivers, Walton & Dowdeswell, had to run the pit in 1887, until putting it up for sale in 1895. For some years the pit was worked then finally closed in 1925.

Castle Eden
This pit was sunk in 1840-2, and many people owned it. Messrs. Cook & Co. operated it in 1856, and then it was taken over by the Castle Eden Coal Company. There were always major water problems, but this stabilised in 1881, this allowed an increase in coal production. The pit closed shortly after. It re-opened in 1885, worked by Castle Eden Coal Company, but the pit once again flooded in 1893. Hordon Collieries Ltd. bought the interests in 1900, quickly controlling the water problem, but it closed due, to not being viable

Chester Moor
Sowerby & Phillips first worked this pit, which was initially called, Chester South Moor, prior to 1880, Thiedemann & Willis taking over after this date. A sinking took place in 1889, after which Priestman Collieries Limited worked it. Prior to 1930 there was 403 men working there, after this date, there was over 700 employed, until 1960, the Brass Thill being the main coal seam. The pit finally closed in 1967.

Chilton
Stobert & Co. sunk the pit in 1872, by 1879, it was owned by, South Durham Coal Company. The main seams worked were The Five Quarter, Harvey and Brockwell. Water was a major problem, but in 1881, new powerful pumps were introduced allowing an increase in production. The lease was strangely allowed to expire prior to 1884, and the landowner, who was Lord Eldon, took possession in this year. The pit was dismantled in 1893, but in 1893 came into the possession of Bolckow & Vaughan. The Five Quarter and Main, was tubbed off, and a further shaft was sunk to the Brockwell. Pease and Partners took over running of the pit in 1924, closing it in 1930. Dorman and Long took it over and re-opened it in 1934, and they worked the Main and Five Quarter. Some of this coal together with coal from Leasingthorne, was coked at Chilton, there was a final merger with Dean and Chapter in 1960, the pit finally closing on 15th. Of January 1966

Chophill
Beamish second pit.

Chopwell
Called the Maria, and worked since, 1795, after which the Taylor pit was worked in 1798, the Conclusion in 1799, and North Pits in 1800. George

22

CHILTON

Silvertop of Ministeracres, working them at this time. It appears the Marquis of Bute, took over operations in 1860, and later rights were secured for Consett iron company, in 1891. Later 3 shafts were sunk in 1894, 1898, and 1909; coal was mined by the long-wall system, using Blackett's conveyors. A drift was put in to the Tilley, at Whittonstall, in 1907. 3000, tons of coal a day was produced at the Chopwell pit, but after the 1926 strike No. 2 shaft closed. Production faltered by 1933, and the drift was expanded, at the East Townley, and the Whittonstall drift, which was obsolete by 1940. In 1959, No.3 pit closed, followed by No1, in 1960, drift mining continued until finally the pit closed in 1966.

Clara Vale

Owned by the Stella Coal Company, the main shaft was sunk to the Brockwell in 1890-3. Also part of the group was Stargate (1800), Emma, (1845), Addison (1864), and Blaydon Main, (1884). A Parson fan, was fitted to the pit in 1897, which was turbine driven. By 1951 the following seams were worked, Five Quarter, Tilley, Ruler, Stone Coal, and the Brockwell. Manpower in 1930-1940 was, 980, by 1950, 590 men. In 1966 Clara Vale closed.

Cold Knott

This pit was worked by 2 shafts one either side of Mown Meadow Road, and was worked in 1857. Harperley Colliery took over most of its operations, in 1897, and the mining centred on about Cabin House. By 1921, it was linked by tub line, to Craig Lee Pit. In December 1924, Cold Knott finally closed.

Copt Hill

(Possibly Houghton-Le-Spring)

Cornsay

This pit was sunk in 1868, worked by, Ferens & Love, mostly drift mining, was operated. High & Low, Colepike, Hollinside Terrace, Lanchester, Ford, Throslenest Plantation, Chapel Flat, Ragpath, and Ravensbush. After water problems, the Ford Drift was flooded in 1885, At Margery Flats, farm and Low Mill drifts extensive draining was carried out, in 1891, which succeeded in draining most of the pit. Bricks were also produced, from 3 Belgian kilns, they also produced sanitary pipes. In 1930 the pit employed 300, lack of trade forced a short closure, in 1938, and by 1950, manpower had reduced to 47, the pit finally closing in September 1953.

Coxhoe and Quarrington Hill

William Hedley first worked this pit in 1832, and in 1836, the engine Pit was sunk. Messrs. James Morrison & Co. the owner of Ferryhill Iron Works, and Thrislington Colliery operated this pit after 1836.

Charlotte Pit, Walker above   Coxlodge Colliery

above Cornsay Colliery

Clara Vale

Craghead

William Hedley appears to be the first to sink a shaft here; he later formed a company called, Thomas Hedley & Bros. And they sank the William pit in 1839, then the Thomas, in 1841 to work the main coal. The Fortune (Sykes) was sunk at Burnhope in 1845, and the George, in 1854, the Oswald to work the Hutton in 1878. Two other shafts were sunk; The Edward in 1909, to work the Hutton and, this was worked lower to work the Brockwell in 1919-20. There was also a downcast shaft sunk to the Busty, in the years, 1916-18. Later two Companies merged to work the collieries, Thomas Hedley & Bros. & South Moor Collieries Ltd. When the National Coalboard took over, the pit was completely overhauled, including the use of Electricity, in 1955-1958. Around about 1963, production fell, and a coal sheerer was introduced into the Busty, in 1966, which took out the remaining reserves, which left only narrow seams of the Harvey and Brockwell. The mine finally closed in 11 April 1969.

Crook Colliery

This Colliery was worked in 1856, by 1879, it was worked by Messrs. Chapman & Morson, after 1897 it was disused.

Crook Drift

Locally Known as the Hole in the Wall Colliery, and worked by the Craggs family. W. Craggs being Managing Director, and his family, Ernest, Alan, Harold, and Flora, helped to run it. Test Bores were put down in 1936, after which a drift was put in. The pit employed 102 in 1939. Prior to closing in 1964, the Hutton and Victoria, was worked.

Crookhall

This was owned by the Consett Iron Company, prior to this the pit was a Latter Day Saint Pit, who worked it in 1857, they expanded it in 1896, but by 1921 it was not used, and infact replaced by the Victoria, which was sunk in 1921-1926. The Woodside Winning and Humber Hill Winning were also part of this group. The Brockwell and Busty, were worked in 1947, and the Brockwell and Townley, in 1959, and by 1963 the main pit closed. In 1964, Woodside Drift closed, but in 1965, the Crookhall Company Ltd, worked the pit on a small scale. Directors of this Company being, A. Marr, R. Knowells, and G. Hodgeson.

Dawdon

The Castlereaugh, was sunk by Lord Londonderry, he sank two shafts, Castlereaugh (19 March 1900-10Sept. 1907), Theresa (17th. April 1900-5th October 1907), both shafts were sunk using the freezing process, Messrs. Gebhardt & Koenig, were credited with the sinking, they also planned to take reserves of coal under the North Sea, outside the reach of Seaham Pit. Major modernisation was carried out in 1953, 1957, and in 1960. A new

CRAGHEAD

below Church Colliery Wallsend

winding system was introduced, by two tower-mounted, multirope friction drum winders, underground diesel locos, followed, then power loading with coal ploughs. Dawdon pit was described by the then Minister of Fuel & Power, as a Jewel in The Crown of the Coal Industry. He also said that the pit was a classic example of what could be achieved. The High Main, and Yard seam were worked in 1970, four years later in 1974, there were 1,742, Manual workers producing 1,579,000, tons of coal annually. There was a series of offshore borings made in 1975-76, which pointed to two underwater anticline dome shaped structures, and these effected reserves of coal, later water effected tunnelling at Zone 29, sea drift, which led to the pit closing on 25th. July 1991.

Deaf Hill

The Trimdon Coal Company sank 2 shafts in 1877, after a short period the pit closed but in 1885 re-opened, by Trimdon Coal Company. In 1889 there was an explosion of no.4 and no. 3 surface boilers, when one man was killed. In 1891 no. 3 shaft was sunk, but in 1919 the workings were flooded, and the no.1 and the no 2 became the main source of production. No. 1 was used for, coal drawing, and as a downcast, for air, the no 2 was used for man riding and also as an air upcast. The Hutton seam was closed in 1944, when 160 workers were transferred to Blackhall, Wingate shared surface operations in 1955, and there was also a rail link. In 1964 a new loading facility for lorries was added, to transport coal to Billingham, this made the railway obsolete. The reserves of coal de-minished in 1967, leading to the closure of the pit, the same year.

Dean & Chapter

Balckow & Vaughan & Co. sank the No1 and No. 2 shafts in 1902; the shafts were completed in 1904. Later the pit was taken over by Dorman & Long in 1929. During Nationalisation it was worked hand in hand with Leasingthorne, in 1950, and also Chilton in 1962. In 1950 the Top and Bottom Busty, and also the Harvey were worked by Jib Cutters, with a system of Long-wall, a skip winder was used to raise the coal in 1956, the pit finally closing in 1966.

Derwent

Richardson owned this pit, at Medomsley; the Derwent Iron Company, which later was known as The Consett Iron Company, sank the shaft in 1853. The Busty was worked with 450 men in 1890, this figure including boys. In 1930 the pit employed 1,094 men, in 1960 only 324 was employed. The pit finally closing in 1964.

Dinnington(Wide Open)

The Agusta, Pit Opened 2nd. October 1867; there was a further sinking of the Hester Pit & West Pit in 1901-1902. The Colliery was owned by John

29

Dean & Chapter

above **Deaf Hill (Trimdon)1904**   **Dinnington Colliery**

Barnes and Partners, who sold out to Hartley Main Collieries in April 1938. The N.C.B. took over the reigns in 1947 until the Colliery closed February 1960.

Easington

Mining started here in 1899. In 1910 the first shaft was sunk using the freezing method. The North, (946, Fathoms) South (250 Fathoms), West (250 Fathoms), the latter shaft was used mainly for ventilation. At first the pit was worked on the Bord and pillar system, later long wall was used, and then in 1950 power loading was introduced. There was a terrible explosion at Easington on 29th. May 1951, when 81 men died. The pit was modernised in 1958-1975-1981, skip winding, with merry-go-round, trains. Seams used at the time were High Main, Main, Yard and Low Main. It was said that Easington had reserves of 8.4 million tons of coal; British Coal included the pit in the 31 pits, which was destined to be closed. Michael Heseltine announced this, on 13th. October 1992. This decision was reviewed but on the 19th. Of October, it was still included on the list of the final 21 of these pits. On the 15th. Of April 1953, the miners voted not to enter the pit, into the Modified Pit review Procedure. The work ceased at the pit on 7th. May, with the face J23 Idle, even though there were good reserves. R.J. Budge attempted to purchase the pit but this fell through over pumping costs. Finally British Coal decided to cease pumping at the Colliery, and the pit was taken out of operation shortly after.

East Hetton (Kelloe)

In 1836 the East Hetton Coal Company sank the North Shaft. There was further sinking in 1856. By 1873 the Five Quarter had been worked out, after which the pit was sold to Walter Scott in 1880, it was then linked to Trimdon Grange Colliery. The Main was finished in 1887, after which work was concentrated on the Low Main, Hutton and Harvey. There was an inundation on 6th. May 1897, which killed ten people. By 1930 the pit was modernised, when all coal was mechanically cut, there was also a dry cleaning plant erected in 1933. East Hetton Collieries Ltd. worked the pit from 1935 to 1946. Power loading was introduced in 1959, with a new winder introduced in the South shaft. After test drillings it was found that 100 million gallons of water, in Thornley Tilley goaf, was very near to the Busty, and threatening the reserves of that seam, and the pit finally closed in 1989.

East Tanfield

This was a James Joicy sinking, in 1844 with two shafts, the Busty and Brockwell. In 1890, 390 men and boys were employed at the pit, when producing output of 170,772 tons annually. In 1917 ownership passed to East Tanfield Colliery Company Ltd., but passed from them to the South

East Hetton (Kelloe)

above **East Hetton**

below **Eppleton**

Derwant Coal Company, in 1929, after it had been closed for a year. There was 899 employed there in 1940, but fell away to 520 in the year 1960, the pit finally closing in 1965.

Eden

E. Richardson sank the Eden Colliery in 1844, but was later taken over by The Derwant Iron Company, named later Consett Iron Company. The coals being mainly used for the Iron works. Production started just after the First World War, with a series of drifts. The Hutton (opposite St. Ives Church), The Main, Castle, Water Level (Near Newhouse Burn), Colliery and Deacon. In 1962, The Eden worked closely with, South Medomsley, and a Colliery drift was completed in 1962, and there was also work carried out on the surface. The Harvey ceased operations in 1976, and the Busty was worked with 298 men. The pit was not mechanised, but decreasing coal reserves caused the pit to close on 18th. July 1980, loosing 180 jobs, 65 of these being transferred to Marley Hill & Sacriston.

Edmondsley

Samuel Tyzack & Co. worked this pit in 1850, when it was called, West Edmondsley, later called Edmondsley Colliery Wellington Pit. The main seams were The Hutton and The Busty, with half of the output used for coking, the pit closed in 1921.

Eldon

A shaft was sunk in 1829, to work the Main Coal, in 1829; alternative shafts were sunk to the Harvey, and Brockley, in the 1860's. The John Henry was sunk to the Hutton in 1890, and this was known in 1897, as the Old Eldon Colliery. Pease & Partners took over the operation in 1903. Eldon old colliery closed in 1931, and Eldon was discontinued, in 1939.

Eldon Drift

The Eldon Hope Drift was worked from 1934, until closing in October 1962.

Elemore

The Hetton Coal Company sunk two shafts in 1825-27, Lady George, (downcast, divided by brattice, into two) and Isabelle (up cast). An explosion occurred on 2nd. December 1886, when 28 people died. There were two companies running the pit, over the years Lambton and Hetton Collieries Ltd., ran it in 1896 and Lambton Hetton & Joicy Collieries in 1924. After Nationalisation the pit became linked with, Hawthorne, which was used as a central coal drawing shaft, which was sunk in 1952-58, this formed an association with Murton and Eppleton. In the 1960s a washout caused, the Busty to be drastically reduced, which led to its closure on 1st. February 1974.

Elvet

The Crawford family sank this pit in 1823, and this was expanded with the

ELDON

ELEMORE   below Evenwood Colliery

sinking of The South Engine Pit in 1858, to work the Hutton. The pit was worked using the pillar system, which caused subsidence and problems with housing, in the district, and this led to a court case, which led to the collapse of the company in 1908. The site is now used in science, by Durham University, and there is a tree trump fossil, and also a water level near Prebends Bridge, with another one in Pimlico, these being exposed in April 1997.

Eppleton

Originally owned by the Hetton Coal Company, along with Hetton Lyons, and Elemore, was sunk in 1825-33, Jane (Busty), Caroline (Main Coal, man riding shaft), a further shaft was added in 1870-74 which was the Lindsey or new shaft. Later the pit was incorporated into the, Lambton and Hetton, Coal Company, then later Lambton Hetton & Joicy Collieries. There was Arc wall cutting in use, with American, loading machinery in use, in 1840. On the 6th. July 1950, there was an explosion, which killed 9 men. Later a new drawing shaft was used at Hawthorn, and after a merger with Murton, the pit closed in 1986.

Esh Hill Top

Nicknamed the 'Take', was between, Millgate cottages, and Low Esh, R. Holliday worked it for Ushaw College, it was leased from, Sir Walter Smyth, and worked in the 1880s. It was principally used for domestic purposes by, the College, and in the 1890s was worked by a drift. Later it was sub-leased to Sir. S.A. Saddler, on promise to supply the College with coal and coke, and there was also an Ariel link to Saddlers Malton Colliery. In 1913, two miners were killed by gas. The pit closed in 1961.

Esh Winning

Joseph Pease sank a shaft, north of Priest beck, it was not completed until 1865-66, because of water problems, and the pit was also worked by drift mining, at this time. The Main coal was declining, by 1919, so the work was concentrated on the Five/Quarter, Hutton, Ballarat, and Brockwell. The colliery closed from 1930 to 1942, in was considered at this time using the pit as a main, drawing shaft, linking the pit with Waterhouses and Ushaw Moor, but this never happened. In 1962, the Ragpath drift was closed, and the Esh shaft was still used for travelling, later the Tilley was exhausted and there was problems with North Top Drift Busty. By 1968 the pit employed only, 230, who were producing mainly by hand hewing, 1,400, tons of coal a week. Financial losses forced the pit to close on 28th. June 1968.

Etherley

The Pheonix Pit worked by Henry Stobart and Co. Old Etherley, in 1840s. There were also two other Etherley shafts, The George, (Escomb), The

EPPLETON COLLIERY

EPPLETON   below ETHERLEY

Jane, near Witton Park Iron Works. The Jane ceased operations, in between 1887-1897, and the George was disused between 1897-1920, the Jane was restarted finally closing in 1925.

Evenwood & Tees Hetton

To the West and East of Evenwood Village, sunk in 1834-45, but in 1836 was sold to the Durham County Coal Company, finally closing in 1840. The property of Armstrong and Co. in 1869, but was taken over by Messrs. Charlton, then to Tees Hutton Coal Co., from 1883 to 1891. Evenwood passed on to North Bitchburn Coal Company, before finally closing in 1895

Felling

Opened by Charles Brandling, in 1779, was operated until, 1811. Two shafts, the John and The William, operated the Low Main commencing, in 1810. There was a terrible explosion on 25th. May 1812, which killed 91, a further explosion on 24th. December 1813 killed, 22 and on the 23 October 1821, six were killed. In the 1850s, Messrs., Carr, Potts, and Company, worked the pit, and in 1833, John Bowes and Partners, bought the pit. The Low Main worked until, the 1890s, together with the Maudling and the Hutton. The pit closed in 1931.

Fenhall Drift

A drift was put in, in 1954, to work the Townley Seam, and kept going until, 1963, the coal was exceedingly high in Sulphur, and thought not to be marketable.

Fishburn

Shafts No.1 South, and No. 2 North were sunk in 1910-13, by H. Stobert & Co. using Bourgii cementation process. Robey Winders were used with four Bowstock, self-firing boilers. Coal was brought to the surface from the Low Harvey, No1, while the No2 Harvey was used for man riding. Coking was carried out on site, and in 1919, there was 50 Duplex Ovens, with a by-product plant also. A Baum Washer was built in 1934. The Harvey, Top Busty, and the Brockwell were the main workable seams, using the long wall, machine cut, hand-filling technique. Joy loaders were also used in the Brockwell on bord and pillar. W.D. Becker Underjet, coke works came into operation, in 1954, while in 1956, major modernisation went on at the pit, the shafts were deepened, and their function reversed. In 1970, nip-out, conditions were noted in the South Winning. The Harvey was finally exhausted and there was geological faults in the Busty, and also the Brockwell, finally leading to closure on 1st. December 1973.

Fallonsby (Wardley)

In the year 1855, John Bowes and Partners, consisted of No1 Shaft-No 2 Shaft, The Maudlin and Hutton were worked, south of the Tyne, finally closing in 1911. The main Falsonby (Wardley No1) was sunk in 1911-12. In

Colliery & Coke Ovens, Fishburn. 8778

FISHBURN

below FALLSONBY

Folionsby Pit, Wardley Colliery. 1542

Above Ferryhill Station with the Colliery in the background. The Station was an important Terminus for the whole of the North East:

Men walking home from Dean & Chapter Colliery:

the early years of the Great War, it closed but re-opened, 1942. There was a proposal put forward in 1948, to combine the pit with, Usworth, but this did not happen until, 1958, when there was a link underground with an installation of a 1960 H.P. Loco. A new winder (Ward Leonard) was installed in the No.1 Shaft, instead of the 700 h.p. Geared AC parallel drum winder. Later Usworth was used for man riding, and Wardley for drawing coal. The work was concentrated on the Harvey and Busty, at Usworth. On the 8th. August 1974, work ceased within the group.

Framwellgate Moor

Northern Mining Company, sunk this pit in 1838-41, had only one shaft, the Company finally collapsed and it was worked by, W.Hunter, & Partners, and Thompson & Green, but by 1859, become under the control of Lord Londonderry, operated by him as a subsidiary, under the name of Framwellgate Coal Company, and later as Framwellgate Coal & Coke Company Ltd., when the Hutton was worked. By 1870 it was about exhausted and the Harvey was opened up. In 1908, The Durham Main, and Caterhouse, which had been associated with Framwellgate, was abandoned, because of geological problems. The Harvey coal was still being sold in 1923, but the pit was put up for sale, and the same year discontinued.

Gordon House

This pit was worked by W.H. Hedley, & Co., from Norwood, when shafts were sunk in 1856, and 1879, on Cockfield Fell, a new Colliery, further south that finally closed in the 1940s, replaced This in 1921

Grahamsley

Another name for North Roddymoor, (Billy Row), where the Lucy Pit was sunk by, Joseph Pease, in 1846. A large fan was operated in the shaft by, 1921.

Greenhead

This was an original Iron Ore, pit for the furnaces of Tow-Law, in 1840. There were no surface workings, and during the years 1865-1897, it was worked on a small scale, by drift work. By 1921, it had closed completely.

Greenside

Simpson worked this pit, in 1880, the Main Pit being sunk in 1902, at the time worked by Stella Coal Company. By 1947 the Brockwell was worked, and the Tilley in 1950. In 1930, - 1940, 1,035 men worked at the Colliery, this manpower fell rapidly to 990, in 1950, 520 by, 1960. Over this period the following seams were abandoned, Victoria, 1951, Crow, 1952, Top Busty, 1953, Three Quarter, Bottom Busty, and Brockwell in 1956. After the closure of Clara Vale, there was an obvious threat of water, which led to the closure in July 1966.

COUNCIL SCHOOL, GREENSIDE 6.

above **Greenside**

below **Hartford Colliery**

44

Hamsteels

Joseph Johnson sunk this shaft in 1868, he was also the owner of Durham Brewery, also T.M. Reay, the owner of Hamsteels, Collieries. They were also known as the Taylor and Busty pit. The Busty and also the Brockwell were at the time worked, and there was also a drift to the Harvey in 1890, infact a series of drifts were worked, The Clifford, West Harvey, and Hall Harvey, near Wilkes Hill. These were worked from 1890 to 1920, but by 1939, all were disused. Ariel cable was used to link these drifts to Hamsteels. In 1932 the Colliery was taken over by Sir S.A. Saddler, and finally closing in 1958.

Hamsterley

In 1864, Dr. W.H. Watson, worked this pit by way of a drift, to work the Top Busty, Three Quarter and Brockwell, and an additional drift was driven in to locate the Busty seam. The John shaft was sunk in 1908, when under hanging tubing was used, the Hamsterley Coal Company operated at this time. In the year 1930 there was 379, men working, by 1950, 260, and by, 1960, 225. By 1963, output was greatly decreased from Park Row Tilley, which threatened closure, but extra reserves were found in the Derwant Colliery Area. Eventually the pit was completely worked out, and the pit closed on 2nd. February 1968, when the men were transferred to Marley Hill and Elm Park Drift.

Handon Hold

Part of West Pelton Colliery, with the Alma Pit at Grange Villa. There was 2 sinking's in 1857-60, and these shafts were worked by James Joicy, all being part of the Lambton, Hetton and Joicy Collieries. There were further sinking's in 1898-1901, to the Busty with a drift to the High main in 1915. Coke ovens were constructed in 1948-52, for the Tilley and Brockwell, and there was also a surface washer added in 1953-56, after the seams were completely worked out the pit finally closed, in March 1968.

Harroton

Mining was carried out here in the 17th. Century. The Lambton family originally worked the pit until the sale of the Joicy in the year, 1896. Two shafts were located near to Nova Scotia, called, The Big, and the Billie, shafts, the Colliery was nicknamed 'Cotia' 940 tons of coal a day were mined from the Maudlin and the Hutton, and in 1913, 700 men worked the Colliery, by the system of Bord and Pillar. Haulage was reorganised in 1947-50, by 1950 production had decreased, and a coal plough with armoured face conveyer, in 1962, did not improve productivity. The pit had major roof problems, which finally led to its closure in 1965.

Hartford

The Athey Pit opened 3rd. March 1858, followed by the Daisy and Scott,

HARROTON 1880

below Haswell

Haswell 1880; below Haswell miners 1868

Haswell miners 1860s

pits in 1866. First owned by Joseph Lamb & Partners who sold out to Cramlington Coal Company. They eventually sold the Colliery to Hartley Main Collieries in 1929. The N.C.B. took over when the Colliery produced 232,000 tons of coal that year. The Colliery finally closed 1961.

Haswell

A test bore was put down through magnesium limestone, in 1811, leading to the engine pit being sunk in 1831. The Little Pit followed in 1833, which was operated by The Haswell Shotton & Easington Coal Company, which worked the Five Quarter, Main and Low Main, and Hutton. The 1844 Strike ended for Haswell miners having to accept the owners terms and conditions. The owners introduced a new monthly Bond' The Durham & Northumberland Miners Association', suffered a near fatal collapse. Members were victimised and had to leave their employment and go to other Collieries. For years they suffered terrible oppression from Coal owners. After the terrible explosion at the Colliery On the 28th. Of September It was alleged that it was the fault of a viewer. At the inquest the accident was deemed to be an accident on the direction of a Coroner: Production started on 11 March 1835, and exported from Seaham, on 2nd. Of July 1835, of the Little Pit, killing, 95. In 1896-97, the pit was closed and dismantled, but Hordon Collieries Limited later opened the North Pit, in 1900-1904.

Hebburn

The A. Pit was sunk in 1792, to work the Main Seam, it was owned by a number of people, Messrs. Easton. Anderson & Partners, in 1857-60, Tyne Coal Company in the 1880s, and Wallsend & Hebburn Coal Company, in the 1890s. In 1884 there was a fire, when the Heapstead was destroyed, during this period the A. Pit acted as a downcast, and the men were raised from the C. Shaft. The Beaumont and Low Main were worked out, in the early part of the century; the Five Quarter, Six Quarter, Hutton and the Yard quickly followed this. The pit finally closing in 1932.

Hedley Hill

Charles Attwood's Weardale Iron Company, in the upper Deerness Valley, operated the pit; there was a drift link, at Hedley Hill Fell. The production was mainly aimed at coke to feed the Companies Iron Works, at Tow Law, from Beehive ovens Sir C. Furness & Co., bought the company in 1899. Then re-named it Weardale Iron & Coal Company. The pit closed for a while in 1904-1906, after re-opening the pit the coke ovens were not re-lit. The Colliery closed twice more in 1929 and 1940, but mining was carried out on a small scale with 26 men, until finally closing in 1966.

Hedleyhope

There were test borings carried out in 1836, after which Joseph Pease

HEDLEY HOPE   below HASWELL 1895

Heworth Fanny Pit

below Hetton Colliery

HETTON COLLIERY

Drawn on Stone by J. D. Harding   Printed by C. Hullmandel

sank the Edward pit. In the 1880s it was worked by, the Hedley Hope Coal Company,

Hetton

Mr. Mowbray sank the pit, in 1818; the pit was stopped because of quicksand. Restarted in 1821-22 by The Hetton Coal Company, having at the time 2 shafts, The Minor and The Blossom, there was also The Lyons Winning, in 1857. An explosion occurred on 29th. January 1836, when 20 men lost their lives. There was a further explosion on 26th. December, when a boiler exploded, 22 men died and 24th February 1845, when 29 men died. Messrs Joicy Coal Company, took over the Colliery in 1911, and consolidated the New Company as, Lambton Hetton, and Joicy Coal Company, Limited the pit finally closing in 1950.

Heworth

There was mining active here in 1758, when it was known as Mr. Blackets Colliery. Extra shafts were sunk in 1819, 1876, 1890, The Heworth Coal Company operated the colliery, the shafts were called John, Ada, Fanny. and the coal was shipped from Tyne Staithes, at Pelaw. The Colliery closed in 1963.

Hordon

There was 3 shafts, North, South, East, these being sunk by Hordon Collieries Limited, in 1900-08, using the cementation process, through Permian limestone, North being a downcast, to the Hutton, seam, the South, downcast, to the Low Main, and the East, to the Hutton being an up cast. North and the South were used to draw coal, the east being used as a man rider. There was man-riding cars introduced in 1919, and major developments at the surface included a Baum Washer and dry cleaning plant, which was updated in 1955 and 1960. Shortages of labour and materials caused a drop in output in 1940-5, and after being Nationalised power loading was introduced, by arc-shears, with chain and belt conveyors. There was an explosion on NE 5 district plough face that killed one, and injured two, on 23 March 1953. Major improvements, were introduced in 1966-7, skip winding at the North shaft, stone winding was done by mine car, at the South shaft. In the 1970s, coal was transported in the zone 6, from the high main, and yard. In 1985 there was water and roof problems that effected production. The pit closed in February 1986.

Houghton

The Earl of Durham sunk this pit in 1827-31, to the Hutton. An up cast was added in 1865, There was explosions, on 1 September 1827, killing 7; 11th. November 1850, killing 27, and also 3rd. June 1885, killing 12. By the 1870s the Hutton, and Main were being worked, but had extensive faulting. Joicy took over the pit in 1896, and by, 1905 the Hutton was worked out.

Hordon Colliery

Houghton

below **Heworth**

Houghton Meadows which was owned and worked by the Londonderry's, was worked in 1896 was re-opened, and worked from 1936 to 25th, March 1960. The Five Quarter was finished by 1952, The Maudlin and Low Main by, 1964, the work then was concentrated on the Busty with Sheerer Power loading. Eventually there was only the Harvey left and the coal had high sulphur content, and finally closed on 26th. September 1981.

Hunwick
The Hunwick & Newfield Coal Company, sink and worked a shaft here in 1854, later in 1870, it was taken over by Bolckow & Vaughan and Company. There was an explosion in the Victoria and a putter was killed, in 1912, the pit closed in 1940.

Hylton
The Wearmouth Coal Company sank the pit in 1897-1900. There were three shafts, The East and West for drawing coal, the South being an up cast shaft, where a 25 ft. Waddle Fan ventilated the pit. The Brass Thill, and Hutton was worked in 1970-1, but geological conditions, reduced the coal to a very thin Harvey, further attempts to establish the Yard seam, were subject to a washout, the pit finally closed on 13th. July 1979.

Inkerman
Mining was carried out in a small way here in 1858, and there was further sinking in 1873. J.G. Wild operated the Inkerman in 1886; he was former Manager of Hedley Hope Coal Company. The pit was worked out by 1897. Black Prince coke yard was extended in the vicinity of Inkerman, around about this time, and the Inkerman Drift, operated, by the Inkerman Colliery Co. Limited, opened in the 1930s. The operation appeared to be closed in the 1940s.

Iveston
Black Reay & Company sunk a shaft in 1839. Jonathan Richardson & Partners operated the pit from 1857, and then it transferred to the Consett Iron Company, by 1884, when it was worked until 1892. There was a bequest of the Coal Royalty, by the Clavering Family, to the local people, when there was small land sales taking place. The Harpers worked Boggle Hole drift, from 1890-1902, and in 1915, Neasham's drift operated.

Kibblesworth
The pit was sunk in 1842, and by 1850 it was operated by John Bowes and Partners, when the Robert shaft was worked. In 1935, The Glamis shaft was sunk, which was linked to the Robert. There was a drift driven in 1965-6, when a belt conveyor was used, this was used to eliminate the use of shaft winding. The pit was further extended by drift when it was connected to Ravensworth Ann, in April 1973. There was ever increasing thin seams, where the 301 rank coking coal was situated, leading to the final closure

Kibblesworth Colliery. 1931

Kibblesworth

Langley Park

General View, Langley Park.

and loss of 622 jobs on 4th. October 1974. Kibblesworth Colliery was linked to the 'River Tyne', by the Bowes Railway (Gravity Line), which was an engineering marvel of the day; this shortened the route to the 'Tyne Docks', over the great Ridge of grit. Many exhibitions of this amazing railway survives today:

Kimblesworth

The pit was started and shaft sunk by The Charlaw & Sacriston, in 1873, when infact 3 shafts were sunk. The Old, and the Busty, being drawing shafts, and the third sunk in 1894-5, was sunk for pumping purposes. There was a shaft accident on 16th. August 1885, when 3 men were killed. Drift mining went on in 1913, when work was concentrated on Brass Thill, Hutton and Busty, after a while the seams were gradually worked out. The Low Main and Brass Thill in 1953, The Harvey in 1954, and the Hutton in 1958, Main 1961, High Main 1965, Five-Quarter and Busty in 1967. After getting a C. pit listing in 1965, it eventually closed on November 4th. 1967.

Lambton

The Earl of Durham, operated two shafts, The Lady Anne which was up cast, and the D. that was sunk, 1831, as a downcast, this was also known as Bourn Moor, also had coke ovens, and washer. An old shaft, William Henry, situated on the east bank of Break Neck Gill, supplied further ventilation. Joicy purchased the pit in 1896. The Maudlin, Five Quarter, and Low Main were worked in 1913. Lambton employed 200 miners from, the Meadows pit, Houghton, when it closed in 1963. Dr. D. Ried, (National Coal board), announced that, 2.4in, seams were not economical, which led to the closure of Lambton D. in February 1965. After excavations, in 1995, timber wagon ways were found, together with coal handling platforms, and other remains that dates from the 1780s, also land reclamation in 1995, led to the pit closure in 1995.

Langley Park

This was owned by, The Consett Iron Company. Three shafts were sunk in 1873, and 1875, outliners also at Kaysburn, in 1889, and Hill Top, in 1904. This allowed mining to progress from The Busty, Hutton, Brockwell, and Brass Thill. Production was geared to coke in beehive ovens, for Consett Steel Works. The ovens were badly damaged in 1904, with the collapse of a Hill Top shaft, but were replaced with Otto Ovens. In 1914, the Brass Thill was exhausted, but in 1930, the Five Quarter and Victoria were expanded, followed by the Harvey and The Main, but they were gradually worked out. Five Quarter in 1952, Busty 1955, Brockwell, 1963, leaving the Harvey and The Victoria, finally the Victoria was abandoned then final closure on 31 October, 1975.

Leasingthorne

In 1836, Messrs King, Mearse, and Campion, agreed to work coal in the Township. This was a two stage pit, originally shafts were sank 1842 & 1843 to work the upper seams. The pit then was owned by a number of owners, James Reid in 1841, Andrew Spottiswood, in 1845, Messrs. Backhouse and Company also Nicholas Wood, and Company, by 1856, and Bolckow Vaughan and Company, by 1870. The Five Quarter and Main were worked, in the 1890s. New Shafts were sunk in 1901-1903 to work the lower seams. The Colliery was large also having Brick works and Coke ovens, employing 1000 men and boys, producing 300,000 tons of coal per annum. Dorman and Long took over the reigns in 1929, but after Nationalisation, the pit was merged with, Dean and Chapter, in 1950, finally closing in October 1967.

Lintz

The Lintz Colliery Company sunk the Lintz and also the Anna Pit, (Messrs McLean & Prior) in 1855, these were worked by McLean until, 1885, when it was laid in, restarted in 1889, by John Shields, who worked the Busty, Three Quarter and The Brockwell. The South Garesfield Colliery Company took it over in 1899, finally closing in 1929.

Littleburn

North Brancepeth Coal Company, sank the Engineer shaft in 1870 to the Busty. The Merchant quickly followed this to the Brockwell, in 1871. It was linked underground to Broompark, which was sunk in 1870. The Merchant was not worked between 1881 and 1893, when coal was drawn from the Busty shaft, this carried on until a stone drift was put in linking both pits. The Company went into liquidation in 1931, but after a while re-opened by Bearpark Coal & Coke Company Limited that worked the Busty. After a while flooding from the nearby River Browney, caused closure in 1950.

Lizzie

The Ritsons, sank the Lizzie & Five Quarter in 1861, the Brass Thill, was also worked. The Willie shaft was sunk in 1866-7, to the Hutton. Work was concentrated on the Little Hutton with a second shaft, at Shield Row, in 1877, the pit finally closing in 1927.

Lumley & Cocken Hall

These were a series of pits that were worked at Lumley, dating from the 1790s. one of these being the George, where there was an explosion, on the 9th. October 1819, which killed 13, a further 14 were killed on 25th. October 1824. Other shafts were First, Second, Third, Sixth, Seventh and Eighth. The second was sunk by way of stages, reaching the Harvey in 1872, at 76 fathoms. The Forrest pit was Downcast; the Sixth was idle for most of the 19th. Century but restarted in 1864. The sixth pit was the only one working in 1896, and the Third pit was converted to Lumley New

Below Marley Hill:

Marley Hill Colliery Pit ponies retired after closure Bullet, Darkie, & Baldie.

MARLEY HILL COLLIERY.

Mainsforth Colliery | below Morrison Pit Annefield Plane

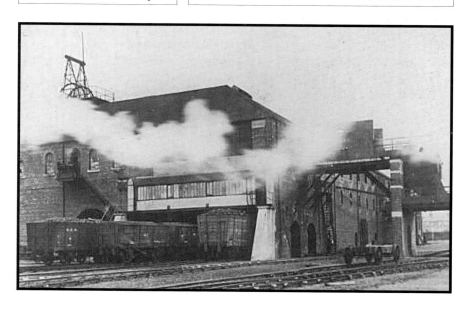

Winning in 1910, when it was worked in conjunction with the Sixth.

Lumley Sixth

Lord Joicy worked the Lumley Sixth, which later became part of Lambton Hetton and Joicy Collieries Limited. There was an inundation on 18th. December 1946, which killed one, the pit finally closed in 1966.

Mainsforth

The Colliery was originally worked between 1872 and 1876, but work then ceased, and was restarted by The Carlton Iron Company, in 1904, with new plant, and also coal cutters, by 1906. Dorman and Long taking over the operation in 1923, when work was concentrated on The Harvey Busty and Brockwell, which was followed by the Hutton in the 1950s; In the 1950s the main was worked with a new loco drift. In 1963, there was a serious financial loss when work was directed to the Main, Low Main and Top Busty. Pumping ceased at Dean & Chapter, in 1967, when the water ran into Chilton, and Leasingthorne. In September 1967, water flooded the low Main at Mainsforth, which led to the pit closing on 3rd. December 1968.

Marley Hill

Grand Allies, worked the North Bank Colliery in the 18[th]Century; John Bowes and Partners Ltd sank the main shaft in 1849-51. The Busty and Brockwell were worked in the 1890s, when 2/3rd. of the coking, was done on site. There was a new man riding shaft sunk in 1955, the West Shaft, with production continuing from the Busty and also the Brockwell, when pneumatic picks in a bord and pillar, system was used. At the same time The Harvey and Tilley, had Reisshakenhobel, ploughs, onto armoured face conveyors. Cockburn Drift was also developed at this time which was linked to Marley Hill which allowed coal to be sent directly to Derwenthaugh Coke works. After 1981, geological problems were found, which effected production; decreased reserves caused closure in 1983.

Marsdon

The Harton Coal Company, using the Kind-Chaudron Process, sank Whitburn Colliery in 1874-81; they later bought the Marsdon coal Royalty, where they worked under the sea, to work the Bensham. A battery Loco was introduced in 1953, to replace the rope haulage. A shaft was sunk in 1958-9, by the new winding system, by 1962, the pit was fully mechanised, with two disk Shearer's and two ploughs. An accumulation of financial losses, and geological problems led to the pit closure on 31 May 1968.

Medomsley

Edward Richardson & Co. sunk the first shaft in the 1839, but by the 1850s it was taken over by the Consett Iron Company, which was known as the Busty. The output of coal in the 1890s was made into coke in waste heat ovens. The Isabelle shaft was sunk in 1898. Two drifts were driven in to the

Main and the Hutton, between 1896 and 1921. In 1962 Medomsley shaft was closed, and Elm Park Drift was driven in. The seams were very thin and the coal was obtained by, windy picks and coked at Derwentthaugh, for use mainly at Consett. By 1970 the Busty was just about worked out, and Three Quarter, coal was opened up, the pit finally closing 6th.October 1972.

Merrington

The Spennymoor pit operated in 1839, by Edward Richardson & Company; by 1897 it was not in use. The pit was re-opened but finally closed in June 1927. In 1880, the Rock Colliery, or North Close Colliery was sunk, around about 24 men working there, producing for the local market. There was a problem with the shaft that collapsed in 1911, but was restored in 1919, and re-named Merrington Park Colliery.

Middle Beechburn

Worked by Middle Beechburn Coal & Coke Company, it closed in 1894.

Middridge Drift

The Weardale Iron &Coal Company worked this pit, together with The Eden 1872, the Charles, 1874. A drift was worked from 1954 to 1966

Milkwell Burn & Broad Oak

The pit was sunk in Woodland at Milkwell Burn, near Broad Oak Farm, south west of Chopwell. Sinkings were carried out in 1856 and 1898, but the area had been previously worked, still working in a small way in 1919.

Monkwearmouth (Wearmouth)

Messrs. Thompson Pemberton and Company, sank the A. and B. shafts, in 1826, the Maudlin was reached in 1835, the Hutton in 1846. Messrs. Bell & Company bought the pit in 1847, and in the 1880s, worked under the name of Wearmouth Coal Company. In 1906, the C. Pit was sunk. In the first half of 1960 the pit was modernised, there was a tower mounted friction drum winder over a new D. shaft, intended for the reserves under the North Sea. The work was then concentrated on the Yard seam, together with the Maudlin and Low Main. J.T. Boyd, the American Mining Company, estimated that the pit had 56.2 million tonnes of reserve coal, with a pit life expectancy of 35.1 years. Michael Heseltine included Monkwearmouth, in his closure list of 13 October 1992. On 19th. Of October it was one of ten in the final consideration, finally closing in December 1993, with a loss of 670 jobs. Knowing about the reserves private enterprise was interested in the pit, when a Nottingham Company, R.J. Budge, also Caledonian Mining, put in bids for the pit. Budge withdrew in March 1994, after British Coal removed machinery, from the pit, shortly after Caledonian, pulled out after finding out the extent of pumping costs, they also discovered a high content of Chlorine, in the coal, there was also a threat of heavy competition from Ellington Colliery on the local markets, the union never accepting these

Montague Colliery

Murton Street showing Colliery in background around 1800

reasons as being valid. All working ceased on 8th. July 1994 at the Yard G.G.5 seam, and the pit was dismantled. The site was used for the Sunderland Football Club, new stadium.

Montague

Montague Colliery in its History has been plagued by water problems. It was first known as Caroline or Francis pit. The View Pit was opened at Scotswood in 1750 when owned by William Benson. The ownership progressed to William Benson & Sons until they were finally taken over by the 'National Coal Board', in 1947. In May 1925 there was a second inrush of water after a previous one in 1888. The water came in this time from the shafts of the old 'Paradise Pit', 38 lives were lost. The pit finally closed in 1959.

Morrison

Thomas Hedley & Bros. Sank the Morrison North and South shafts in 1869. They were also part of the Louisa Old, and New, and the William shafts. In the year 1925, the Holmside and South Moor Collieries Limited controlled them. There was an explosion on 22 August 1947, when 19 people lost their lives, 3 others died months later. In the 1950s the pit merged with South Moor. The South Pit closed in 1961, and the North pit closed in 1964.

Morrison Busty

Holmside and South Moor Collieries Limited, sank the West up cast shaft, and also East downcast, in 1923-5. There were no coal drawing until after the 1926 strike, actually in 1928. The Townley, Busty, and Brockwell were worked in the 1940s, and in 1947 a German plough was introduced. The Morrison Busty and the Louisa workings were linked in 1956, and there was a general improvement in 1959-60, when electricity was introduced to the winder, new skips and a new washer. The Low Main, Brass Thill, and Hutton, supplied the Louisa coal mainly by windy picks. The Harvey, Top and bottom Busty, and bottom Brockwell supplied the Morrison Busty mainly by windy picks using long wall faces. On 8th. February 1964, the Louisa section closed, mainly through lack of reserves, and faulting in the Harvey, the total pit closed finally on 5th. October 1973

Murton

Colonel Braddyll & Partners, and South Hetton Coal Company sank 3 shafts the East, the Middle (Polka), and the West (New Pit), between 1838-1843, intending to work the Hutton. There was an explosion on 15th. August 1848, which killed 14. The West Pit was modified in 1922 when a Koepe winding plant was set up. There was a further explosion on 26th. June 1942 which killed 13. Later in 1959 the pit merged with a new drawing shaft at the Hawthorn pit, which was sunk in 1952-8, and went into partnership with

below **Leasingthorne Colliery**   above **Murton 1880s**

South Hetton in 1983, and Eppleton in 1986. Production at the time was concentrated on the C. pit and the High Main and Harvey; chainless haulage was used with web shears. Later there were roof problems, and increasing costs led to final closure on 29th. November 1991

Nettlesworth

Messrs. Jonasshon & Co. worked a colliery here in 1856, by the 1880s the pit was worked by, Elliott & Hunter, by 1896 it was closed, and the work concentrated at workings at Black Burn, which was near to Nettlesworth Hall but by, 1920 it was disused. In the 1930s, 3 drifts were driven in, the West, Pump, and Railway drifts. Nettlesworth Dene Drift worked from 1945, until closing on 27th.September 1974, because of lack of reserves.

New Brancepeth (Sleetburn)

Mining was carried on here from 1850, near Scout's House Farm, for Brodie Cochrane, in 1856-8 when 3 shafts were used. Weardale Steel Coal & Coke Company Limited took over operations in 1933, when with rite and barites was also worked. A washing and milling plant was added in 1911. Barites, was used in making white paint for bleaching flannel and shoddy cloth and also asbestos goods. Witherite is used for making barium compounds, in the manufacture of wallpaper and also linoleum. The Busty and the Ballerat was worked out by 1934, the Brockwell and also the Tilley by 1944 and 1952, and by this time the output was only 400 tons a week, the pit finally closed in June 1953.

Newfield

This pit was sunk in 1840 for John Robson and Partners (Newfield Coal Company), these were the Robson and the Burnett shafts. The coal was transported via the West-Hartlepool docks by rail. By 1870 the pit was taken over by Bolckow Vaughan & Company. At this time the Busty was worked with 2 Drifts to the Harvey and the Beaumont. The pit later merged with Byers Green, and later took over by Dorman and Long Company Limited in 1929. After Nationalisation the pit was still operated by Dorman & Long Steel limited in 1954-1959. Newfield drift finally closing in March 1963.

New Herrington

There was mining in the Philadelphia (New Herrington) area in the 18th. Century with the Margaret (Peggy) pit the Dorothea (Dolly) pit followed in 1816. The Earl of Durham bought the pit in 1819. The Five Quarter and Maudlin was worked in the Dolly, while the Hutton Five Quarter and the Main was worked at the Peggy. In 1874 the pit was modernised, and the sinking of the Lady Beatrice (New Pit), which had 2 shafts. This brought an output of 1,600 tons of coal a day, by the end of the 19th. Century, this production was maintained by using the best possible machinery. 23

Shildon Colliery Sidings   below New Brancepeth

NORTH SEATON COLLIERY. (1478).

Seaton Colliery

below **Low Moorsley**

Low Moorsley

New Hartley

below North Biddick

workers were drowned in the Peggy pit, on the 3rd June, 1885. The Peggy finally closed in 1930, but was maintained for ventilation purposes. The Dolly closed in 1958, work carried on into the middle of the 1950s, using power loaders, and skip winding until finally closing in November 1985.

New Shildon

The Shildon Coal Company Limited, operated this colliery, and the working seams were the Busty, and Brockwell, in the 1890s. Shildon Colliery closed in June 1928, New Shildon closed August 1965.

Newton Cap

The Colliery was sunk and operated by W.C.Stobart & Company, in 1859, it was also called Toronto Colliery, and by the 1880s it was operated by Henry Stobart & Company. By 1894 four seams had been located and worked they were Five Quarter, The Harvey, Constantine, Brockwell. The pit was closed in 1920-1930, but the North Bitchburn Fireclay Company Limited, re-opened it in 1937 and employed 119 in 1950. The pit closed in 1967.

North Biddick

This pit was being worked as early as 1700, when there was an 80-fathom shaft. Miners holed into an old drift on 18th January 1743, when gas in the goaf was ignited killing 17 people, there was a further explosion on 6 December 1773 when 19 people were killed. Sir George Elliott worked the pit in the 1880s.

North Bitchburn

A shaft was sunk in 1840 to work the Brockwell. At this time Henry Stobart & Company worked the pit. This changed to the North Bitchburn Coal Company Limited, and from 1934, the North Bitchburn Fireclay Company Limited, in 1930, employed 202 people. By 1940, 150, 44, were employed by 1960. By 1966 the pit closed.

North Brancepeth Collieries

There were 2 collieries in the group, Littleburn and Broompark. The Company North Brancepeth Coal Company went into liquidation in 1931.

North Hetton Collieries

The Hazard and Moorsley pits were part of this group, run by Hetton Coal Company. Joicey took over the Company in 1911.

Norwood

Mining was carried on here in the 18th Century, a colliery was leased to the Earl of Strathmore, in 1807. There were various partnerships after this, until a lease was taken by the Durham County Coal Company in the 1830s. The Northern Coal Company also took out a lease on the Colliery, until its collapse in the 1840s. Norwood Coal Company ran the pit from 1869, it was run by Miles Bruce, John Todd, Michael Brown and John Hedley; the

Thrushwood was also part of this group. The pit was finally put up for sale in 1898, re-opened again by Dunston & Swalwell Colliery, in 1900, when it operated until 1931, finally closing in that year.

Oakenshaw

Straker & Love sank the Brancepeth B. Pit in 1855, finally closing in 1967.

Old Durham

A shaft was sunk in 1849, to work the Hutton and the Low Main. It finally closed in 1893.

Old Etherley

Owned by H. Stobart & Company.

Ouston

Messrs. Hunt, Perkins & Company worked this colliery early in the 19th. Century. There was an explosion on 3rd. November 1817, when one person was killed and three badly burned. There were 4 shafts A.B.C.E. E.M. Perkins was the principal owner, & also owned Birtley Iron Works, and Ouston and Urpeth Pits, working under the title of Pelaw Main Colliery Limited, from 1926. The B. worked from 1824-1875. Ouston E. was modernised, with air compressors and electricity, in 1914. Ouston and Ouston Winning came together on 20th. May 1916. Three seams were worked by 1928, by 1,200 men and boys, at the E.pit. On the same pit a new winding engine was installed the same year. Finally the E. pit merged with the C. pit in 1957. The pit finally closed in January 1959.

Pagebank

Also known as South Brancepeth, the pit was sunk in 1855, the shaft being divided into three by the use of brattice. Two partitions being downcast of air, one being up cast. There was a fire in the shaft on 30th. September 1858, which killed 10. The pit at the time was owned by, West Hartlepool Dock & Railway Company. Bell Brothers operated the pit by 1879, Dorman & Long & Company, taking over in 1923. Reduced Reserves of coal from the Busty and Brockwell finally closed the pit in July 1931.

Pelaw Main

The Perkins family (Birtley Iron Company) operated this colliery along with Bewick Main, Ouston, and Urpeth. In 1906, the group were known as Owners of Pelaw Main Collieries Limited, shortly after a French Syndicate, took them over but after the occupation of France and Paris the Company collapsed in 1940.

Pelton

Messrs. Kingscote & Company sunk this colliery, but later James Reid & Partners, Messrs. Swabey & Company, and Messrs. W.C.Curteis & Company operated it, until 1860. W.J. Hutchinson, operated the pit from 1866, when the Hutton was worked with the Busty just started in 1865.

Above Okenshaw, below testing for gas at Dean & Chapter:

Pelton Collieries

Philadelphia

Below **Percy Main Colliery**

There was an explosion on 31st. October 1866, which killed 24. Lord Dunsoney & Partners, operated the pit in the 1880s, and in 1901 it was controlled by the owners of Pelton Colliery Limited. In 1928, it was placed in the hands of the receivers, when a possible sale to Arthur Kellett & Son fell through, and the workings were dismantled, in 1929, M.H. Kellett, re-started the pit, under the name of Mid Durham Coal Company, who were the operators of Pelton Fell in 1932, there was a cage accident in the same year when 3 men were killed, the pit finally closed in February 1965.

Pensher
George Elliott, leased the site, from 1864 to 1879, the Earl of Durham took over operations when the D.pit was sunk in 1931.

Pittington
The Buddle, Adolphus, Londonderry, and Lady Seaham were part of this group owned & Operated by Lord Londonderry. Between 1856 and 1897, the Buddle closed, and the North Hetton Coal Company then operated it. The Londonderry & Adolphus, closed in 1891, and after the 1912, strike the Lady Seaham was not re-started.

Pontop
There was a number of pits operated around this area, The Spring Pits, The Hive, The Bog, and the North pit near, Bantling Castle, Pontop South Pit was situated west of Annfield Plain, and the Moor Pit near Harelaw, Staple West Kayo, Pontop Pea, south of Whiteley Head, Success Pit, at Pontop Pike, which was an air pit in the late 19th. Century, which was ran in the 1930s by, R.Southern of Hamsterley House, Dipton. John Bowes and Partners were also working in the Pontop area.

Rainton & Letch Collieries
This group covers the following collieries, Adventure, Resolution 1816-19, Nicholson 1817, Plane 1817, Meadows, 1821-4, Letch (Alexandrina, 1823-4 near Moorsley.

Ramshaw
The Earl of Strathmore, operated this colliery from 1807, and by 1830 there was 4 shafts, A.B.C.D. By 1942, The Ramshaw Coal Company Limited, mined here from 1942, the pit finally closing in October 1959

Randolph
The North Bitchburn Coal Company, near the Wigglesworth Fault, sank the pit in 1893. The Brockwell was ventilated in 1893, by a 30 ft. Waddle fan, there were double Decker cages, there was also a Luthrig washer, and jigging screens, and also cocking was carried out in Coppee Ovens. Pease & Partners took over operations in 1927, but the Randolph Coal Company took over in 1933, after Nationalisation a new drift was driven in to the Hutton in 1953, the Pit finally closing in February 1962.

Roddymoor Colliery

Randolph   below Ryhope Colliery

Ryhope

below end of shift Roddymoor

Ravensworth

Mining was carried on here from the 18th. Century, fifteen men and boys were killed by gas on 10th. June 1757. The colliery was owned by E.M.Perkins, owners of Pelaw Main Collieries in 1906, these also operated Betty & Shop pits, Team Colliery, in the 1950s, the Ravensworth Ann was added in 1930, also the Ravenspark Drift, in 1936. Ann's Metal and High Main seams closed in 1960, when work was concentrated on the Tilley using ploughs. In February 1962, the Ravensworth Shop closed, and in 1968 all coal drawing was done at Ravenworth Park. The Ann and Kibblesworth were linked underground in April 1973, when surface workings were finished at the Ann pit.

Roddymoor

The four working main seams in the 1840s were Main, Five Quarter, Ballerat, and the Yard. The pit was sunk by Joseph Pease, to work the Main. Two other companies undertook leases in 1851 and 1873. In the early half of the 20th. Century there was around 1000 men and boys employed, by 1940 there was 1055, employed. The Pit amalgamated with Wooley, after Nationalisation in 1951, the pit finally closing in 1963.

Rough Lea

Henry Stobart & Company, sunk this colliery in 1858, later operated under the name of North Bitchburn Coal Company Limited, finally closing in 1926, re-opened later under the ownership of Pease & Partners, until 1931.

Ryhope

First sinkings were done in the 1840s, and the pit was further developed in 1905. The Maudlin, Low Main, Hutton, and Harvey was worked in 1913, and by 1933, the pit was modernised, the present winding engine was replaced by a 500 hp, electric Frazer & Chalmers engine, it was further modified with a Tower Mounted multi-rope, friction drum winder, in 1950. In the 1950s the seams operated were, Five Quarter, Low Main, Harvey and Busty. In 1960, the output was 26cwt, per man shift, but shortly after in 1963, the Busty and the Harvey were stopped, and work was concentrated on the Five Quarter, this led to financial losses culminating into forced closure on 26th.November, 1966.

Sacriston

In 1839, the Victory pit was sunk, as a downcast to the Five Quarter, and an up cast to the Main. By 1881 the Main was worked out, also the Five Quarter in 1884.There was a linking of Sacriston and the Witton Pit, underground at the Busty level, in 1882, and there was a drift driven in 1900, The Shield Row Drift. There was an inundation, on 16th. November 1903, which killed 3 miners. Shield Row, closed in 1940, and in the 50s & 60s, the Brockwell, and Victoria, were worked, with the main coking coal of

Seaham Collieries

above Sacriston

Shildon Datton Colliery

the Victoria, being 20 inches thick, which was hewn with windy picks, and Longwall faces, the coal was processed at Derwenthaugh, in to coke, for foundry use. Following the strike 1984-5, declining reserves, geological problems, and also a request by the men to cease mining, probably the threatened loss of redundancy benefits, was a factor, influencing the final closure outcome, all work ceased on 15th. November 1985, until final closure on 28th. December 1985

Seaham

This was a Lord Londonderry, colliery, sunk in 1845-9, enabling the first coal to be produced in 1852. Seaham had the No1, and No.2, shafts, with the No.3, at Seaton, and the group was known as Nicky- Nack. On the 25th. October, there was an explosion which killed 26, a further explosion happened on 8th. September 1880, which killed 164. The pit was completely modernised in 1958-63, with skip winding, at the No.1 shaft, an electric winder, at the No 2 shaft, with a new coal preparation plant. Mining concentrated on the Five Quarter, E., Maudlin H., Low Main J., where there was drum shears, and trepan. On 11th. July 1983, the pit merged with, Vane Tempest, when production was concentrated on reserves from the C. seam, with conveyance via. the Seaham Skip winder. To enable the use of coal for Power Station use, from Seaham management prepared the surface accordingly. Colliery consisted of the following; below 1/ 'Seaton Colliery', known as the 'High Pit', No. 3 Shaft and at the time of sinking was owned by the 'Hetton Coal Company', sank by William Coulson on 31st July 1844; began in ernest 12th. August 1845. 2/ The 'Low Pit', Number 1 & 2 shafts; above was owned by the 'Marquis of Londonderry', and was sunk 13th. April 1849; producing coal by 27th. March 1852. By November 1864 Seaton High Pit was sold to the 'Londonderry Family' and traded as one Colliery to comply with Legislation:

Sherburn

The Earl of Durham sank the first shaft in 1828, and later the Lady Durham shaft was added, in 1873. In January 1914, the Sherburn Collieries were taken over by, Messrs. Samuelson, & Company, who at the time operated the Newport Ironworks, Middlesbrough. This Company worked the Low Main, and Lady Durham, until finally closing in 1921.

Sherburn Hill

The Earl of Durham sank two shafts, in 1830, and 1835, these were the North, and the West, to work the Hutton. Like Sherburn it was took over by Samuelson in 1914, he worked the Low Main, Main and Busty, later in 1923 it was took over by, Dorman & Long. In 1951, a surface drift was put in which served as a downcast, with the west shaft, while the North Shaft was used as an up cast. Four other shafts added to the ventilation.

Sherburn House Colliery   below Sherburn Hill Colliery

Shotton.

Shotton Colliery above

Seaton Delaval

FORSTER PIT. NEW DELAVAL. 4224.

Manpower profile reported that geological faults, would effect its economic position, but even so the production increased to 23 cwt., per man shift, working the Harvey, Five Quarter, and Busty. 65 men were transferred to coastal pits, and the Colliery closed in August 1965.

Sherburn House
Again an Earl of Durham pit, sunk by him in 1840 to the Hutton. The coal was coked at the lady Durham Pit. Again took over in 1914 by Samuelson, who sunk to the Busty. The pit closed in 1940.

Shildon
R.Surtees, to mine thin coal, sank the main engine pit in 1830; he completed a further sinking in 1831. The pit was commonly called 'Dabble Duck'. Later Bolckow Vaughan & Company, worked the pit, and they sank the Furnace shaft, in 1864. 200 men and boys were employed in 1908, though it was known that the seams were thin and unprofitable, finally closing in 1937.

New Shildon Colliery
Sunk in 1949, closed in 1965.

Shildon Datton Colliery, Sunk on Surtees land & worked by Bolckow & Vaughan. The Brockwell seam was worked, 5 feet 6 inches in this area. It yielded 800 tons each working day in the 1890s. Datton was active from 1830 to 1924, Apparently it acquired its name because of Irish Pitmen; when asked where they worked they replied "Dat', un". Was served by the Surtees Railway which was a branch off from the S&D Railway at Shildon Station. Later the Shildon Boy Scouts converted the Pit heap to a playing field in memory of the Boy Scouts who lost their lives in the war:

Shincliffe
High Shincliffe, or Shincliffe Bank Top. Bell & Company sank the pit in 1837; there was an explosion on 17th December 1840, which injured 5. Joseph Love & Partners worked the pit in the 1860s, it finally closed in 1875.

Shotton
There were two pits sunk in 1840-4, The Engine Pit, and the South pit, these were worked by Haswell, Shotton & Easington, Coal & Coke Company Limited, and were abandoned in 1876-7. In 1901 it was re-opened by Hordon Collieries Limited, at the time having two shafts the North & South. By 1913 the three Quarters was worked out, leaving the Main, Low Main, Hutton, Harvey and Busty still working. Production peaked in the 1920s, producing a million tons, annually, but there were losses in the 1950s, which led to the endless rope haulage, being replaced by Diesel Loco, and also the introduction of Mine Cars. In 1958, the Coke yard closed. In 1971, they hit on a novel idea of blending the Yard coal and the

above Datton Gates at Shildon

below New Seaham

Silksworth

below St. Hilda's South Shields

High Main coal, but later as reserves in the Yard seam diminished the pit closed on 1st. September 1972.

Silksworth

Lord Londonderry operated this pit, sinking the No.1, shaft, and the No. 2 shaft, in 1869-73. Later in 1920 Lambton & Hetton Collieries Limited acquired it. Major modifications were carried out in 1948-58, with an electric skip winder, and re-enforced concrete headgear. The Hutton was worked out in 1970, when the miners were transferred to the Harvey. Geological problems led to the pit closure on 6th. November 1971.

South Derwent

This pit was operated in 1856, with a sinking to the Hutton near to Annfield Plain. There was an additional shaft near to the Smiths Arms, Catchgate, called the Stewart, and there was also a staple at Carmyers. R. Dikinson & Partners operated the pit in the 1880s, together with the West Shield Row pit. Between 1856-1884, the Willie was sunk, north of the Hutton. South Derwent finally closed in March 1950.

South Durham

Known as the John Henry Pit, they were comprised of Eldon Old Colliery, and South Durham, they were operated in 1856. The South Durham Coal Company took over the operation in the 1880s, they also ran Eldon, in 1920, and South Durham Colliery was also known as Eldon.

South Hetton

The South Hetton Coal Company Limited sunk this pit in 1831-3, working the Hutton from both shafts, later in the 19th. Century production was concentrated on the Five Quarter, Main and Hutton, known as South Hetton, Walls End. Later the South Durham Steel & Iron, Company Limited, operated the pit prior to Nationalisation when there was a drop in production, after Nationalisation it improved, when there was a general improvement with machinery, which was completed in 1953. This involved electrification, new winder house, and Hapstead, and new concrete headgear. The Pit was connected to Hawthorn, underground and a proposal to merge with this pit was put forward, but did not materialise until, 1983, having been proposed in 1965. All of the Main Coal was drawn at Hawthorn, and also processed there.

South Medomsley

In 1893, a wooden shovel was found in old workings suggesting early mining. Two shafts were sunk here the Ann (1864), Mary (1867), there was also a drift where the Hutton coals were drawn, and The Main and the Busty were drawn at the Mary Shaft. The owners of The South Medomsley Colliery operated this pit in the 1880s, by 1887, a Five Quarter Drift had been driven in, and the Mary had been merged with a drift, in Pontop Low

Burns Colliery Where Accident Occurred West Stanley

Burns Pit Stanley

below South Moor Colliery

# Dates of Sinking of North East Collieries

SOUTH PELAW COLLIERY.

South Pelaw

Stanley Louisa Pit

89

Wood, by 1896. A Main Coal Drift was driven in, in 1921, by the Pikewell Burn, also a Brass Thill Drift, east of Pontop Hall, with further drifts to the South West, (Coronation Drifts). Later in 1939 drifts to the Hutton, Low Hutton, and Five Quarter had replaced these drifts. The Pit finally closed in March 1963.

South Moor
Mining went on here from 1818; Thomas Hedley & Brothers, situated north of Stanley, sank Quaking House pit. These pits were later known as Charley and fan pits, the Annie was sunk in 1846, the Mary in 1867. There were other shafts namely the Hedley, and also the William. The Charley pithead was damaged by fire, in 1911, and in the 1950s, the pit was merged with the Morrison North and South, the whole group finally closing in 1973.

South Pelaw
The Perkins family started operations here in 1860, when sinking a 65-fathom shaft, later in 1890-1, a new sinking to the Busty was made, for Thomas Gilchrist; the upper level seams remained unworked. The South Pelaw Coal Company operated the pit until finally closing in January 1964.

South Tanfield
Joseph Smith & Company sank a shaft in 1837, to the main Coal, later in 1870-1, the C. Shaft was added. In 1880, there was further sinking, to the pit when a sinker, was killed, when travelling in a kibble, between the Hutton and the Brass Thill. James Joicy ran operations, from the 1880s until the pit closed in 1914-15.

Springwell
Lord Ravensworth & Partners carried out the first sinking of the pit in 1824; the first coal was exported from Jarrow Staithes, on 17th. January 1826, there were two shafts at the pit, the A. and the B., On May 9th. 1833, there was an explosion, in the B. Pit when 47, men and boys lost their lives, in the Hutton seam, and in the same seam 27 were killed, on 6th. December 1837. Three men were also killed in the shaft when the cage chain broke, on 9th. March 1840. John Bowes and Partners later operated the pit, but it finally closed in 1931.

Stanley
This Colliery was situated North of Crook, Joseph Pease, sunk the shaft in 1857, when it was known as Josephine, later drifts were added to the pit, but it later closed in 1911.

St.Helens & Trimdon Collieries
At St. Helens; the Engine Pit was sunk by William Coulson, to the Brockwell, in 1830, this was quickly followed by the Emma, to the Yard Seam, in 1831, and also the Cathrine, to the Brockwell, in 1835, a fourth

Thornley Colliery.

Thornley Colliery

below Shotton Colliery

Thrislington Colliery (West Cornforth)

shaft the Tindale, worked the Harvey, these workings were owned and operated by, Joseph Pease, & Partners, flooding was the cause of closure in 1924.

St. Hilda

Locally known as Chapter Main Collieries, first worked by S.Temple, in 1810, but a string of owners followed him, including Messrs. Brown, and Messrs.Devey, Messrs Brandling sank a further shaft in 1822, which reached the Bensham in 1825, later the Harton Coal Company Limited took over operations. On 28th.June 1839, there was an explosion that killed 51, men & boys. A further sinking was carried out at Westoe, in 1909. The Colliery closed in 1940, but the shaft was later still used as an air up cast for Westoe.

Sunniside

Joseph Pease sank this pit in 1866-8. Later there was drifting and airshafts near the River Deerness. It was also associated, in the 20th. Century with the Dickens House Drift, the Pit closed in 1925.

Sunnybrow

The Northern Coal Mining Company sank Willington Colliery in 1840, Straker & Love, working the A. & the B. Pits, later worked this. The pit closed in June 1927, loosing 275, jobs, re-opening in February 1929, finally closing in 1932.

Tanfield Lea

In 1830-1, the Engine pit was sunk by the Marquis of Bute, adding a further shaft to the West in 1839. James Joicy, purchased the pit in 1847, and it was part of the Lambton, Hetton & Joicy Collieries, in 1903, the Margaret Shaft was sunk, the Colliery finally closed on 25th. August 1962.

Tanfield Moor

The Earl of Kerry was responsible for early mining here in the 18th. Century, the first coals being exported from Derwenthaugh Staithes, on 14th. June 1768. The Willie pit surviving well into the 19th. Century finally closing in 1948.

Thornley

John Gully & Partners sunk this Colliery in 1834-5, mainly to work the Harvey. There was a fire in June 1858, without an explosion, when the area had to be drowned to stop it. Work carried on until the Harvey was laid in, in 1861. The London Steam Colliery & Coal Company, took over operations, in 1865. The Company worked under the heading of the Original Hartlepool, Collieries Company, in 1865, and later in 1870-2, sank the Thornley New Winning, to work Five Quarter Coal. There was a surface fire, which destroyed surface operations, on May 8th. 1875, causing the Company to go bankrupt in 1877, they recovered from this but went down

TUDHOE COLLIERY. 1687

Tudhoe Grange

below Trimdon Grange

Trimdon Grange Colliery

Tudhoe Grange below | Above Old Trimdon Colliery

again in 1884, at this point the shaft was filled in, but the Weardale Iron & Coal Company, reopened it in 1888, sinking a further shaft the No2. In 1904, and which from 1914, was the main drawing shaft. Water broke in from old workings from Cassop Vale Pit that took the lives of three men, by drowning. The pit was fully re-organised in 1956, when a new Baum Washer and dry cleaning plant was added. Production finally ceased on 9th. January 1970, officially closing on 31st. January 1970.

Thrislington

The Bottom Hutton was proved in 1835, by a series of borings that year, by 1843, the pit started production, and later was sunk to Main Coal, and later operated as the Mary pit, by the Rosedale and Ferryhill Iron Company, mainly to supply the Ferryhill Iron Works in 1867, until the Company collapsed due to the recession in 1879. Thrislington Coal Company took over operations shortly after, by 1911, most of the Hempstead was destroyed by fire. In 1914 it passed to the North Bitchburn Coal Company, then in 1932, to Henry Stobart & Company. In 1930 there was a work force of 1005, but by 1940 this total dropped, but later peaked to 1,124, in 1950, later in 1960 dropping to 805, finally closing on 4th. March 1967.

Trimdon Grange

Joseph Smith sunk this pit in 1845, to the Five Quarter, in 1846, and to the Main in 1847, then selling it to Matthew Foster in 1852, when it was sunk even lower to the Low main in 1863, then to the Harvey in 1872-3. By 1880 the pit was sold to Walter Scott, who expanded the coking side of the pit. In an explosion on 16th. February 1882, in the Harvey Seam, 69, men & Boys lost their lives. The pit was closed, between 1930 & 1937, and was re-opened by the East Hetton Collieries Limited. The coking side of the business ceased in 1962, even though the pit had a high life grading, A, Category. Operating problems led to proposals for closure in 1967, but was deferred, until 16th. February 1968.

Tudhoe & Tudhoe Grange

The Weardale Iron Company, sunk this pit in 1864-6, the pit had 3 shafts, the East, West, & Success. Tudhoe grange was sunk in 1869-70, by the same people, but was only worked until 1885. An explosion occurred on 18th.April, 1882, which killed 37, men and boys. The pit was mainly run for the local Iron Works. The pit was closed in 1935, but after the second world war was re-opened, under the name of Tudhoe Mill Drift, which operated from 1954 until February 1965.

Tursdale

Borings to prove the coal was carried out in 1854, and then the pit was sunk in 1859-60. Dorman & Long took over operations in 1923, when the pit was combined with Bowburn, and used as a man-riding shaft; it was

Urpeth

below New Heapstead Whitburn

finally closed in 1968.

Twizzell

Early borings were carried out in 1795, to prove the seams, before the main sinking of the Gate Pit, in 1842, when James Joicey operated the pit. Production costs spiralled, and the pit closed in 1934, the neighbouring Alma Pit, (West Pelton Colliery), closed in November, 1958.

Tyne Main

Also called the Friar's Goose Colliery, in 1798-9, the Engine Pit was sunk, and the High Main was abandoned in 1842, still maintaining pumping operations, at Friar's Goose Colliery. By 1860, Tyne Main, and also Woodside, were worked by, Messrs. Losh & Company, 406. Workers were employed and there were three shafts. The pit finally closed in 1926.

Urpeth (C.) Pit

This pit was sunk by William Coulson (later Master Sinker), to the Hutton, in 1831. Messrs. Hunt Perkins, and Company was also working at Urpeth, also in the early 19th. Century. The pit was later run by the Perkins family, who were owners of Birtley Iron Works, later re-named, Owners of Pelaw Main Collieries, Limited in 1906, and Pelaw Main Collieries Limited, in 1926. The Pit was remodernised in 1908, when the Hempstead was renewed, with a Blackett Washer to clean the coal at Urpeth, Busty, and also the C, Pit coal. A surface drift was also driven in, from the surface to Shield Row. The Pit was merged into a group with Ouston E., in 1957, finally closing in 1959.

Ushaw Moor

There was early test drilling carried out here in 1857, 1867, and 1870, and soon after the shaft was sunk. John Sharp operated the pit, in 1873. Later the pit was bought by Henry Chaytor, in 1879, but later in 1883, was sold to Pease & Partners, after a very violent strike, it later closed in 1927 until, 1929. On 14th.November, 1932, there was an explosion that killed 2 in the Victoria seam. There were proposals to close the pit in 1959, and this succeeded, in August 1960. Five Million tons of coal still remained untouched in the Harvey seam.

Usworth

The Colliery was sunk in 1845-7, and at the time was worked by J. Johansson, and also Sir George Elliott, working 2 shafts, the Wellington East, & West. The main shaft was sunk in 1874, and called the Frederick. John Bowes & Partners took over the running of the Colliery in 1882, when the Low Main, Maudlin, and Hutton were worked. On 2nd. March 1885, there was an explosion in the West Pit, which killed 41 men and boys; the Engine House was also destroyed by fire in 1890. In 1891, there was a

Wardley Colliery.

Wallsend below

above **Wardley**

boiler explosion, in the Low Main, haulage engine, which killed 3 men. In 1910, the Victory shaft was sunk, and 49 years later in 1959, it was combined with, Follansby/Wardley. Later in 1961, production was concentrated on the Maudlin, Hutton, Harvey, and Busty, the pit finally closing on 1st.August, 1974.

Vane Tempest

Lord Londonderry decided to sink a shaft here in January 1923, and work began in December, originally they concentrated on 2 shafts the Vane and the Tempest, which were won with the freezing process, being completed in 1926. The C. seam was worked inland in 1976, and later combined with Seaham, on the 11th. July 1983. Dosco & Anderson, road headers, drove in the main gate roadway; further in-bye Eickhoff, double ended in-web shears, were used at the faces. Coal was processed at Seaham, with a small quantity, blended specially for power station use. British Coal included Vane Tempest among the list of 31 pits, to be closed, which was announced by Michael Heseltine, on 13th. October 1992, and was later listed with 9 others subject to 90 days, consultation period. The pit ceased operating with the last shift on 23rd. October, 1992, officially closing on 4th. June 1993.

Victoria Garesfield

The pit was originally sunk in 1860, operated by the Victoria, Garesfield Colliery Company and later purchased by, Priestman Collieries, Limited, in 1899, finally closing on 13th.July, 1962.

Waldridge

Early mining was carried out by William Jolliffe, on Waldridge Fell, in 1779, exported from Fatfield, later in 1831, a further 2 shafts were sunk and worked by Messrs. Sowerby, & Company. By 1870, Christian Rudolph Ferdinand Thiedeman, based at Newcastle, operated the colliery also Owen Wallis, (Northamptonshire farmer). In 1875, the Busty was sunk, and the group continued to operate the pit until the 1880s, and by the 1890s several other people bought interests in the pit. The Main working was from the A. & D. shafts in 1896. Waldridge Fell Old Pit (leased by Priestman Collieries Company) from Hylton Jolliffe, closed in 1911, the A. pit closed in 1926, the D. Pit remained open until 1963. There was Drift mining at Smithy Dene, on Waldridge Fell, which broke into earlier workings, where old timbering, a sledge Hammer, and parts of a leather shoe, were found.

Wardley

See Follonsby.

Washington

First mining is recorded in 1776, in 1882, 14 people were killed in the Eye Pit of Washington Colliery. Mounsey, Backhouse, Cruddace, and

Washington Glebe

below Walker Colliery

Company, carried out early operations, here that were abandoned in 1862. The Washington Coal Company, took up Royalties, at the Oxclose and also the Glebe pits, when the No.1 shaft, and also the No.2 shaft was sunk, in 1901-2. On the 20th. February 1908, there was an explosion that killed 14. By 1970, the pit was fully mechanised, with the use of bi-directional sheerer's. After a short period of time the Maudlin was exhausted, when work was concentrated on the Hutton, which at the time was very thin, its declining quality, meant that it was unsuitable for CEGB use, this led to the closure of the Glebe, on the 5th. August 1972.

Washington F. Pit
This pit was first sunk in the late 1700s, and later operated by the Washington Coal Company, until 1926. Matthew Henry Kellett, a mining engineer, re-opened it and introduced electrification, and windy picks. After Nationalisation, power loading was introduced, when production peaked in 1964-5, to 486,000, saleable tons of coal. The Busty, coal later was exhausted on 9th. March 1968 followed by the Brass Thill, on 21st.June, 1968, which ultimately led to the pit closure on 28th.June 1968.

Watergate
Priestman Collieries Limited, operated and ran this pit from the 1920s; it finally closed in August 1964.

Waterhouses
This was a Peases pit, West Brandon was sunk in 1856-7, using the Mary as a second shaft, to work the Main Coal, and the pit was not productive until 1863. Drifts were driven in, in 1870, and in 1879, the South main, and the North Five Quarter, North Main and the South Five Quarter in 1885, and the Klondike Five Quarter, in 1899. In 1901 the Ladysmith Drift, was driven in from the North Five Quarter, to the Ballarat, Main coal was also worked from the Rowley Gillett Royalty, later a lease to work the Baryta, was took up in 1919. Tests were made in the Okenshaw Exchange Boundary; fault proved 96%, barium sulphate, and the South Ballaratt heading was driven to work it. In 1924 Kelletts Main coal drift, was driven in and by the 1930s, most of the output went to ICI Synthetic Products, Billingham and also Bankfoot Coke Works. To maintain this demand for good quality coal. By 1936, windy picks were used, also scraper loaders, and in 1954, a Gusto Multi Plough, was installed, in order to work the thin seams. In 1963, Ivesley Drift closed and miners started to leave to get work in the Midlands, and Wales, work was reduced to one shift in 1964, with 146 men left. There was roof difficulties in the Victoria Seam, then later there was water problems, and reduced reserves, which ultimately led to closure in August 1966.

Wearmouth

Wearmouth Collieries

Wearmouth_was the last deep mine in Durham County and it closed in 1993.

West Auckland

In 1826, test borings were carried out, and then a pit was sunk in 1838. Messrs. Edmund Backhouse & Company worked the pit in the 1850s, until the 1870s, when Bolckow, Vaughan & Company, took over ownership, working the Harvey, Brockwell, and Busty, in the 1890s. A shaft was cleaned out in 1914, which had been sunk in 1884, at the top of Bildershaw Bank. The Townend colliery closed in 1925, because of flooding, but there was still drifting carried out. The Ramshaw Coal Company Limited, mined here in the 1930s. The Colliery closed in July 1967.

Westerton

Edmund Backhouse & Company, mined in this area early in the 18th.Century, but Nicholas Wood & Partners, operated it from 1841, when it was part of the Black Boy Coal Company, later the pit passed to Bolckow, Vaughan & Company, in the 1870s, the Brockwell and High Main, being the most important seams. By 1924, the Colliery closed but re-opened in May 1928, after which it was making a loss. Dorman & Long took over the pit in 1929. Work concentrated on the Merrington Lane Drift, when work continued, until final closure in 1931.

Westoe

The Harton Coal Company sank a shaft in 1909-11, as an alternative to St. Hilda, Colliery, the latter being the main winding shaft. Westoe came into its own in 1947, when the Yard seam was worked, using the Long Wall system, and by the 1950s, was modernised to work under-sea, coal. A Tower mounted multi-rope, friction drum winder was used over the new Crown shaft, 3.5, ton mine cars, also 12.5, ton battery locos, when work continued with the Main, Maudlin, and Brass Thill, where 270 hp, AM double-ended, ranging drum shears, increased production. The main customers being the Power stations at, Blyth, Drax, Eggborough, Kingsnorth, and Tilbury. Michael Heseltine included Westoe, in his list of closures on 13th.October, 1992, even though it had proven substantial reserves, and the mechanisation was first class. It was later included in the moratorium, on 10 pits, and it was finally closed in May 1993, with 25th. November 1993 planned as the demolition day.

West Pelton

This pit had 2 shafts, the Alma, near Grange Villa, and also Handen Hold Pit, at West Pelton.

West Stanley

Charles Townley, owned the coal Royalty, at West Stanley, in 1842, he leased it to Messrs.Clark, Rayne, Burn, Hawthorne, & Anderson, but it was

Wingate   below Westerhope

worked regular by, David Burn. There were 3 shafts in operation, the Kettledrum, sunk in 1859, the Lamp, 1874, and the New Pit, 1876. By the 1890s, the Shield Row, Five Quarter, Low Main, Hutton, and Busty were worked. In 1891, the Pithead, was destroyed by a fire, later in 1909, an explosion, tragically killed, 168, men and boys. The pit was operated up to 1936, by the South Durwent, Coal Company Limited, finally closed in 1936.

West Thornley
The Weardale, Iron Company owned this Colliery. In the 1890s, employed 350, men & boys, working the Ballaratt, Five Quarter, Top, Main, and Three Quarter seams. The Colliery closed in 1925, loosing 450 jobs, later re-opening in 1937, finally closing on 6th.November, 1965.

Westwood
Consett Iron Company sunk this colliery in 1871, when the bottom Busty was worked, together with the Three Quarter, and the Brockwell. The Pit closed for a time in 1901, because of the depression in coke sales, the pit finally closed in 1940.

Wheatley Hill
The Thornley Coal Company, sank this pit in 1869, three years later in 1871, five men were drowned when water entered the workings from Thornley. The Original Hartlepool Collieries Company Limited, later worked the Pit under difficulties finally collapsing in 1884. One year later it was taken over by the Weardale Iron & Coal Company Limited, when work started on the Harvey, in 1892, later in 1900, a Dunlop & Merideth vertical winding engine, was set up, which was second hand. From 1956, all coal produced was processed at Thornley, by 1965, the reserves of coal diminished leading to the closure of the No1. Pit closing, on 11th. December 1965, when the men were transferred to the No 2. The Quality of coal deteriorated, this, together with financial losses led to closure on 3rd. May 1968.

White Lea
This Colliery was situated near to Crook, and was initially sunk in 1840, Ralph Waters, owned the Colliery in the early 1850s, but was operated by Bolckow Vaughan & Co., in 1855. Pease & Partners took over operations in 1889. According to the 1856, Ordinance Survey map, Old White Lea, west of Billy Row, White Lea Colliery. North of Pease's Bankfoot Complex, New White Lea, to the South West. Later in 1904, White Lea Drift closed.

Whitwell
Abraham Teesdale, worked this Royalty, in the early 18th. Century, together with Mrs. Ann Wilkinson. The Colliery was situated east of Shincliffe, and was made up of 2 pits, A. 1836-7, B. 1840, the latter being sunk as far as

Wingate above

Hutton Henry Upcast Shaft 1898

the Hutton, and operated by the Whitwell Coal Company, Messrs. Wight, Robson, and Ogden. The C.pit was sunk, in 1855-6. In the 1860s, was operated by, White, Panton, Robson & Company, employing 200, men & Boys. In the 1870s, it closed, and later in 1884, when the lease held by J.M.Ogden, was due to expire, there was rumours of a take over which did not materialise.

Whitworth Park

Sank by the Durham County Coal Company, in 1841, to work the Hutton, later in 1842, the Company closed. The west Dock Company later sank the Whitworth Shaft, when it was sold to R.S. Johnson, and T.M.Reay, to work the Low Main, economic problems, lead to its closure, in 1883. The complete operation was sold in 1885, with the Hapstead going to Castle Eden Colliery. Messrs. Brown, & Oliver, continued to work the Low Main in the 1890s. In 1928, a new Whitworth Park Colliery was worked by the Whitworth Park Coal Company, later after Nationalisation, work concentrated on thin seams, with hand filling. Closure was carried out because of exhausted coal reserves on 26th.July, 1974.

Windlestone,

This Colliery was sunk in 1876-1877 for the Pease family. The main shaft sank to the gannister seam 323 feet below the Brockwell; it was then bored a further 195 feet searching for workable coal without success. After the collapse of the coal prices the Colliery lay idle until 1895. This caused the whole village to disappear. As coal prices picked up the village again prospered until 1931, when coal prices again fell it again closed and this time remained closed.

Wingate

Lord Howden & Partners, operated this pit with the Lord shaft sunk in 1839, the Executors of John Gully, later operated the pit when a further shaft was sunk the Lady. The Wingate Grange Coal Company ran the pit during the 1880s, and there was an explosion on 14th.October, 1906, when 24 men and boys lost their lives. Most of the coal was exported and the name of the Coal was well known as 'Caradoc'. Ventilation of the pit was done by, the Lord shaft acting as the up cast, and the Lady shaft acting as the Downcast. A shaft at Hutton Henry, being the Marley Shaft, provided further ventilation. In the 1950s, the Five Quarter and also the Main were abandoned, leaving the Harvey, and also the Tilley, which were worked by, Longwall, and hand hewing. The pit closed on 26th. October 1962.

Witton

Once part of Charlaw Colliery, it was sunk in 1859-60, to the Hutton, and operated in the 1890s, by Charlaw & Sacriston, Collieries, Company limited. The pit was linked in the 1920s, by a drift to Sacriston Colliery.

| Windlestone Colliery (Chilton) | below Sinking Windlestone 1875 |

Wingate

Sinkers at Wooley

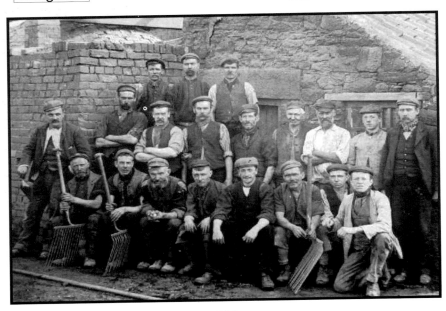

From the 1920s, the Shield Row was worked by No1; and no 2; drifts, near to Sacriston, Heugh, the Sacriston Colliery working the seam near to the Coronation Drift. The Colliery closed on 8th. January 1966.

Woodhouse Close & Tindale (Emily)

The Colliery was sunk around 1842, by Mr. Flintoff, intending to take the remaining coal from the disused Coppy Crooks, Colliery, later being owned by, Thomas Vaughan & Company, the Middlesborough Iron prospectors, around about 1880, the firm became bankrupt, and the pit was sold. Pease & Partners were working Tindale, in `1885, when it was linked to St. Helens, later by 1897, the pit was abandoned.

Woodifield

Situated south West of Crook, and sunk in 1840-3, Bolckow & Vaughan & Company, operated the pit in the 1850s, closing in 1884, and again in 1909. Steels House Colliery Company, Limited, carried out further mining in the 1930s.

Woodland

Messrs. Sharp & Hardy, worked by them until 1837, leased the Pit from the Duke of Cleveland. The Assignees of the late Reverend W.L.Prattmen, took over the lease, and from 1867, was operated by, Messrs. Whitwell Fryer, Grieveson, & Dale (later to be, Woodland Collieries, Company Limited) drifting work was carried out to the Main and the Five Quarter, the Same Company operated Clark Scar (1872) and also progressed Wigglesworth Colliery, which closed 1901 because of lack of reserves. The Cowley Shaft was sunk after which the Company went into liquidation. When New Copley and Langley Dale were sold to 'New Copley Collieries Ltd'. Woodland was taken over by Cargo Fleet Iron Company until 1921 mining on a very reduced scale was carried out until 1926.

Wooley

Joseph Pease & Partners sank this pit in 1864, being part of the Pease's West, group of Collieries. There was a fire on 30th.January 1911, which badly damaged the Washer, and the Coal Hopper. In June 1927, the Colliery closed, but was re-opened in 1929. In September 1931, it closed again, only to restart again in 1937, when Pease & Partners agreed a long-term contract with Dorman & Long, to supply coke, for their needs, and which was the total output of the Colliery. Wooley was linked to Roddymoor Colliery, and finally closed in August 1963. *******

THE GENERAL LAYOUT OF NORTH EAST COAL SEAMS

B etween the years 1958 and 1963 the district around Barnard Castle was re-surveyed after an initial survey in the years 1870 to 1881. I used the survey of the Institute of Geological Sciences, along with other sources to compile my information. In this chapter. An analysis of 168 bores and pit shafts were carried out. I was a little curious in this procedure as evidence suggests that the Coulson side of my family were employed as Sinkers. Because of the fact that Sinkers would have to consider the facts in this survey very carefully when deciding on sinking shafts for the maximum winning of coal-measures. Taking into account yield quality and any Strata faults or hitches that could hinder the smooth running if the pit. On the coal seams mentioned in the previous chapter; I will at this point show the position within the Strata of these seams, their measurement and their height from the surface. These facts would be very important to Coal Engineers & Sinkers in their task of sinking the shafts for the maximum Yield of coal.

Lower Coal Measures:

Bottom Victoria, Top Victoria, Victoria Rider:
Seams measure all sizes 1 inch to 24 inches. The seam also appears in Shildon, Middridge and Eldon area.

Brockwell Coal: is found in abundance in areas around Woodland and Copley, both top and bottom. Brockwell is the lowest major seam to have been worked in the area. At the time of the survey supplies of Brockwell coals are just about exhausted, this shows just how successful the seam was. North of the river Gaunless between Butterknowle and Toft Hill the Brockwell measured between 72-75 inches. Around Evenwood and West Auckland measurements are 48 to 75 inches, and around Randolph and Keverstone Grange, measurements were recorded of 70 to 90 inches. North of Todwell House 60 inches were recorded, but this area was highly disturbed because of faulting, this was found to be virtually impossible to work. As an open cast site at Rowntop farm a 30 ft. thick band of sandstone proceeds the Brockwell coal and at High Wham a 20 inch Brockwell seam is worked on opencast this being 22 feet above the normal Brockwell seam.

The Busty:
In the eastern and central areas the Busty begins to appear both top and bottom, very close to the Three Quarter coal that is relatively a very thin coal, in some areas the Top and Bottom Busty is only divided by approx 8 inches. Top Busty being 816 feet 4 inches and 824 ft.9 inches. At New Shildon Eldon and Middridge top Busty is very variable in thickness usually ranging between 24 and 38 inches. The Busty and Tilley group of coals overall range from between 40 and 50 feet between them. Top Busty is found to be an inferior coal at West Auckland and Tindale and also at Old Eldon, South Church and Coundon Grange and infact sometimes disappears. At Shildon Middridge and Fielding Bridge the seam usually ranges around 24 and 38 inches.

Tilley Group of Coals:
In the Copley and Woodland area the Tilley group of coals appears as a single united seam everywhere else it appears to be thin and inpersistant seam top and bottom.

Harvey:
In the Woodland and Copley areas the Harvey lies between 12 and 78 feet between the Tilley group with sandstone lying 8 to 10 feet under it. The Harvey coal is known locally as The Yard Seam and has been widely worked in this area. Like the Busty the seam is prone to wash outs. Locally and in Eastern parts it divides into Top and Bottom seams usually separated by 8 feet of measures.

Hutton and Bottom Hutton:
The interval between top and bottom Hutton is 130 feet and contains up to four thin inpersistant coals. The lowest coal of the Hutton lies 40 to 60 feet above the Harvey. The Hutton Seam is sometimes known as the four foot.

Middle Coal Measures:
In the Southern half of Durham and Hartlepool the bottom Hutton occurs as a single coal seam of 36 to 38 feet thick. In the extreme North East the seam is generally thinner. The seam has been widely worked in the area. The Top Hutton coal is very thin and of little value.

Low Main :
The Durham Low Main (known as Chatham) can measure up to 63 inches, but generally a range up to 20 or 36 inches is also prone to washouts, especially around Auckland Park.

The Durham Low Main:
The Durham Low Main seam interval has a maximum thickness of 220 feet, averaging 110 to 170 feet; the seam is generally overlaid by shale and sandstone.

Maudlin Coal:
Is a composite seam up to a thickness of 77 inches and up to 70 feet below the Main? The seam generally splits into top and bottom coals which are up to 17 feet apart. In Durham and West Hartlepool both seams become apparent.

Main Coal:
Main Coal is the thickest seam and has been worked more than any other. Where the seam is united it ranges from 36 inches to 132 inches, when the seam is split into two it never exceeds 3 feet. The measures between main Coal and five Quarter Coal range between 47 feet to 120 feet this is mainly made up of sandstone and shale's.

Five-Quarter Coal:
(Bottom five Quarter) is generally a single seam ranging from 60 and 72 inches, the seam is very evident in Shildon and Fielding Bridge in a few localities the seam is absent.

Metal coal: (Jet Dickey Dent or Top five Quarter) usually a single seam measures between 6 to 66 inches in thickness, the term Metal Coal derives from Newcastle upon Tyne. In the Durham area it sometimes becomes united with Five Quarter Coal the seam has a maximum thickness of 26 inches.

High Main:
Occurs as a single seam ranging between 18 to 24 inches in several localities but is generally split into two, these being very close together. Because the Top High Main is generally absent they are identified together as The High Main.

Bottom High Main:
Locally known as Willy Winter. Generally ranges between 18 and 38 inches, but west of Shildon a thickness of 85 inches inclusive of shale and band was proved.

Top High Main:
The Top high Main ranges up to a recorded thickness of 33 inches but is generally between 6 and 21 inches. It has an overlying Sand or Post stone.

The Brass Thill:
The interval varies between_30 and 60 feet and is generally a single composite seam. The Brass Thill coal is commonly overlaid by an abundance of shale's where the seam divides within the strata. The top Brass Thill measures 29 to 44 inches, the bottom 12 to 18 inches, with the division within the strata of 11 feet.

COAL RATINGS
Not every coal was perfect for every use some coals were used for totally different uses as the chart shows. The Durham area produced coals that

ranked from 200h to 702. The best coals have a rating of 200 H - 303H-302H.in a nutshell the best coals were just about void of impurities. These coals are prefixed with the letter H. in such seams as the Brockwell, Victoria and the Harvey that produces this type of quality coals.

One of the main priorities of this coal is it's dust content. In tests The Harvey was ranked very high with less than 5% and never exceeded 7%. The Durham Low Main and Bottom Hutton and the Main Coal also showed a good yield.

Top and Bottom Victoria,		**Top and Bottom Brockwell,**
Top and Bottom Busty,		**Tilley Group of Coals,**
Top and Bottom Harvey,		**TopandBottom Hutton,**
Low and High Main,		**Maudlin Group of Coals,**
Main Coal,		**Top and bottom Five Quarter,**
Metal Coal,	**(Jet- Dickey Dent)**	**High Main,**
Brass Thill	**The Durham Main, Coal**	**(known as Chatam)**

THE COMENCEMENT OF THE COAL INDUSTRY

The Durham coalfield became industrialised at the end of the 17th. Century. With the introduction of large-scale coal mining. It actually started in 1375 when a mine owned by Henry Vavasour's was being worked at Cockfield Fell the mine was one of the first inland mines recorded.

Other coal Fields started to spring up around the North of England namely Woodland, Copley, Butterknowle, Cockfield, Evenwood, Toft Hill, West Auckland, St. Helens, Bishop Auckland, and finally Shildon. Sadly the reserves of coal in this area are just about exhausted, the small areas that remain are worked as open cast under licence from the National Coal Board. This work is being carried out between Woodland and Toft Hill.

There were roughly fourteen different seams worked in the Durham area, and this would be doubled if account was taken of the strata of the earth, when most seams divide into two I/e Top Hutton and Bottom Hutton. Some seams are very narrow and are subject to washouts. Owners and Sinkers would have to determine the best areas for sinking the shaft making sure that they would get maximum and the best coal possible. It was paramount to make sure sample drilling's were made and that these would be properly analysed, the height of the coal together with the thickness of the seam. The exact position of the seam in relation to other material such as limestone, sand stone post stone etc. The latter also being very important to Quarry owners. One of the main priorities of this coal is its dust content. In tests The Harvey was ranked very high with less than 5% and never exceeded 7%. The Durham Low Main-and Bottom Hutton and the Main Coal also showed a good rating. The Phosphorus and

Chlorine in North Eastern Coal is generally lower than other regions and lower than the National average. The rank code of 500 and over was strong coking coal and mainly used for coke ovens or household coal and also used for the manufacture of gas. This coal contained 13% to 15 % ash, and was also very high in sulphur. During the 1950's most mines in the area reached maximum production, one example was New Shildon which raised 290,000 tons, this came from Brass Thill and Hutton seams. Brussleton produced over 171,000 tons in 1957 from the Durham Low Main, Brass Thill, Tilley and Busty seams. Most if this coal ranked from 501 to 602 and therefore general-purpose coal used for coke ovens, gas production house fuel and general steam raising a part of it was also used for ships bunkers.

The stratum in both Northumberland and Durham is much the same in both areas. A large part of the coalfield in South West Durham is flooded in that several million tons of workable coal had to be abandoned, this amounted to some 70, million tons. 75% of this coal it was estimated was coking coal. By 1945 it was found that 25% of the total output of Durham collieries were producing coal that was being used for the production of gas and also being used in other industries such as Iron and steel works throughout the area. By the year 1880 The Durham Coalfield was producing 28,063,346 million tons of coal, not at all bad taking into account the lack of mechanisation in the industry at that time.

COAL RANK	DESCRIPTION	
200H	HEAT ALTERED:	NON-CAKING
303H	HEAT ALTERED:	NON CAKING
302H	WEEKLY CAKING	MEDIUM
301	STRONGLY CAKING.	PRIME
	COKING COALS.	
401	VERY STRONG CAKING	
402	VERY STRONG CAKING.	
501	COKING & GAS COALS	
502	COKING& GAS COALS	
601	MEDIUM CAKING MAINLY	
	HOUSE COALS. INDUSTRIAL	
701	WEEKLY CAKING: HOUSE	
702	INDUSTRIAL	

EARLY COAL INDUSTRY

The Start Of It All

Many references to coal have been said over the Years with regard to Newcastle and the North East in general in particular 'Like Taking coals to Newcastle'. If Newcastle isn't exactly built on coal it is certainly built on the profits from it. From Durham Cathedral in all of its grandeur, to St Nicholas Church in Newcastle with its arched spire, to the humblest miners cottages, all have basically came out of profits from coal.

Seaham Harbour can also be said to have survived on coal over the early years and not on its Harbour, even though it appeared to rise out of the sea. The Marquis of Londonderry owned the collieries in this region, Seaham situated very close to Sunderland. The railway leading directly to South Hetton Colliery a distance of some four miles. Although not a natural Harbour, Seaham was a very convenient shipping station for colliers to fill up with coal, and two piers were constructed solely for this purpose.

Extra houses had infact trebled, the houses at Seaham, these built by Lord Londonderry for people working in his pits in the area; Ships registered to carry coal south to London were eleven hundred, the tonnage amounted to 221,276 tons. Each collier making approx. 10 voyages to London from the North East each year. Sunderland at the head of the Wear also increased its colliers sailing from there, this together with Stockton-on-Tees. Hartlepool was also thriving, combining with the Stockton and Hartlepool Railway bringing coal from inland coal mines, here the docks were laid out just for the job, one being 650 yard long 150 yards wide and another 280 yards long and 130 yards wide, with an entrance to the Harbour of 300 square yards. The drops were ideal for the transportation of coal by sea. In the early 1800's ships were observed sailing to Europe, some sailing to Scotland, and the Norwegian coasts others sailed to Denmark and the Baltic all were notably well down in the water with the weight of the coal, North East pits were indeed paying their way.

In 1852 the first steam Collier entered the Thames having sailed from Newcastle in 48 hours consuming 8 tons of coal on the voyage and her cargo was 600 tons of coal which was unloaded in one day. In the year 1848 a total of 3,599,844 tons of coal was despatched from Newcastle and South Shields of which 1,111,461 tons were exported, the home consumption being 660,000 tons, The River Wear produced 2,409,974 tons of which 498,162 was exported. Seaham and Stockton dispatched 662,044 tons of coal, 105,094 tons being exported. From Hartlepool 1,165,628 tons were produced of which 243,060 tons were exported. It was estimated in 1830 that we had coal reserves of 400 years, but little did experts realise at that time the role that Nuclear energy would play in power stations, this together with the finding of large reserves of oil in the North Sea; Harold Wilson prophesised that England would be self sufficient in Oil by 1980, vast supplies of coal would lie dormant beneath us in our country. Around about 1840 bore holes were tried without success in many other parts of the country, around about Northampton, £20,000 was invested in trial drillings and bores etc. but to no avail there was just no coal in this area and showed the importance of the North of England and in particular Newcastle upon Tyne.

Early Shaft Sinking

Shaft sinking is fraught with dangers and difficulties and these greatly increase expenditure in the early stages of sinking. As early as 1835 there was great pressure on mine owners to have two shafts, the main reasons for this was ventilation and safety. Infact at the end of the Hartley Disaster this was legislated and many lives were saved because of this. Where Quicksand and water feeders are faced, it is not an outside estimate for expenses of up to £80,000 to be run up, and it is absolutely essential that proper surveying and test bores be completed before sinking the shaft. That is why a good Sinker was worth his weight in gold, and his experience could not be questioned. All the sides of the shaft had to be properly bricked up and lined. When every thing is going well a truer estimate for sinking a shaft which was eleven feet in diameter 250 yards in depth would cost approx £5 a yard. This would increase, as the shaft got deeper One of the most expensive shafts sunk in the Tyne Tees area was Monkwearmouth near Sunderland; Messer's Pemberton spent nearly £80,000 on this shaft that was fraught with problems. A similar sinking at Dalton-le-dale, in Durham sunk by the South Hetton Company. In this pit there was almost impassable quick sands and it took many months of labour with steam power of no less than 1274 horsepower to get through it. The owners of this particular pit were very safety conscious and also very enterprising, arranging to sink a further shaft within 50 yards of the first shaft. The second shaft being relatively easier to sink than the first, in that the first shaft drains all of the water if it is within 50 yards of the other shaft.

Operations on sinking the shaft begin by digging out the soil where the shaft is planned, and then a windlass (ancient mining apparatus) is erected. After the sinking has progressed a few yards the walls are re-enforced by laying bricks to secure the sides of the shaft. The cylindrical wall is raised upon a circular framework of wood called a crib. The sinking is then progressed further and the procedure of securing the sides once again is completed. Exactly over the sinking area a triangle frame is built, 20 or even 30 feet high, this is used to get force behind the boring tools.

The borers use a variety of tools very cleverly, when liquid matter is removed because of obstruction, the borers easily remove this and the process is restarted.

When the strata is needed to be analysed this is done by withdrawing the rods which are being used, together with the boring needed for checking, and new implements inserted to progress the bore. Experienced sinkers could quickly sink a shaft and in trained hands the boring tools get through hard rock relatively easy. As boring shafts advanced throughout the years, the use of explosive became more and more prevalent, and with careful placing of the explosive and proper packing of the drilling, top and bottom with explosive placed, the boring hole can be blown in the strata using a precise amount of the explosive, so as to loosen rock within the measurements required for the shaft. Initially the boring tool is put in by hand, two men using the brace head, but as the bore gets deeper a horse gin or steam engine is used, as it gets deeper the cost of sinking obviously gets more expensive.

Accomplished Sinkers can work out what water springs he will come up against and which could slow down the operation. Water is the worst obstacle that they will face, and invariably in the Durham area water brought work to a standstill in a number of cases. Multiple small borings are usually made in succession to checkout coal seams, hitches in the strata. Horizontal borings being easily drilled as these clear themselves without withdrawing the tools. Horizontal drillings are used to check for other pits or workings in the area, this type of drilling was also done to check for gas, which could of accumulated, and boring this way would be needed for winning drifts. Sinkers usually advised colliery owners on the general problems in any particular winning, such as the need for pumps and to what size to control the water that they may come up against. Sinkers usually supplied most of their own sinking gear, such as kibbles, trams, running platforms. It was worth noting that Durham Area Sinkers just about monopolised the skills needed for shaft sinking and these skills were much sought after all over the country, as they grew more and more experienced they took on more and more tasks which a lot of other miners found virtually impossible, not forgetting shafts were getting deeper and deeper as the strata took the coal further and further below us. When Snibston Colliery was being sunk in the 1830's local sinkers had to be replaced by Durham Sinkers whom the owner (Stephenson) sent for, when the Leicester men failed to cope with the large volume of water gushing out of the Keuper Marl. By changing the lining from tubing to brick lining and introducing more efficient pumps the Durham Sinkers stopped the flow of water and reached the Main Coal after 9 months sinking.

119

Sinkers Tools Of The Trade:

1/Brace Head 2/ Common Rod, 3/ Double Box Rod, 4/ Common Chisel, 5/The Indented Chisel, 6/ The Cross Mouthed Chisel, 7/ The Wimble, 8/ The Sludge (for bringing up mud) 9/ The Rounder, 10 The key for supporting the train of rods at the bore mouth, 11/ The key for screwing together and asunder the rods, 12/ The topit, or top piece, 13/ The Beech, (for catching the rod when it breaks in the bore, 14/ The Runner, (for taking hold of the topit, 15/ The Tongued Chisel, 16/ The Right Handed Worm, 17/ The Left Handed Worm screw, 18/ The Finger Grip or Catch: ¬

Difficult Sinking

Hebburn Colliery:

Hebburn colliery was commenced in 1792, this was one of the arduous and difficult sinking's of all. The amount of water drained amounted to 3000 gallons a minute. At first tubing had to be done by wooden planks, which for a while stemmed the water. After some time this started to leak as the years progressed, and these had to be replaced by cast iron segments which did the job far more effectively.

In the early days of the pit there was many explosions, mostly by being naive on the reasons why explosions occurred in the first place. At the time, they often saw streams of blue flame emanating from the furnace at the bottom of the shaft, they never showed alarm neither were they aware of any immediate danger. On occasions there were disastrous explosions. The furnace at the bottom of the shaft was used for ventilation purposes; the method of ventilation at that time was ill understood. The furnace using a brattice drew the air. This air had to travel about 30 miles, before its exit, to the surface and at that time the air would be foul.

Around about 1810 a general creep overtook the whole colliery, and this caused a suspension for a long time. A creep was a kind of subsidence of the strata, from immense pressure. In some parts this naturally caused a rise in other parts of the strata and there was a tendency for the floor and the roof to approximate. Gasses (inflammable) were greatly increased and no ventilating furnace was safe. Shortly after an air pump was tried, it was five feet square and worked by a steam engine; it produced a good current of air. Although while running, it produced the desired effect it was subject to breakdowns and stoppages. An interesting fact of this colliery at Hebburn was that gas was taken from the blowers at the colliery and the celebrated chemist C. Ellison made his experiments for safety lamps and infact the first lamps were tested in this very pit. The colliery at this time, being owned by Easton & Co. and the coal worked at the time was 'Hebburn Main'.

Gosforth Colliery:

The colliery lies about 3 miles north of Newcastle. Sinking commenced in 1825, the winning completed Jan. 31st. 1829. The High Main seam was subject to the great Ninety Fathom Dyke. The High Main Seam was reached at 25 fathoms below the surface and then dipped to 1100 fathoms 1200 at the hitch. At this point the coal was not very good quality at the dyke, so the shaft had to be sunk to a further depth of 181 fathoms perpendicular in order to reach the lower level of the coal. It was found that in most of the coal seams past through while going deeper, at the point of the Dyke these seams were under Quality. It took a horizontal drift of 700 yards long to reach quality coal and a great deal of the sinking was, through solid rock.

Eppleton Jane Pit:

This was another difficult sinking. The sinkers had to go through sand gravel limestone and solid rock. Water was also a big problem this was running at 360 gallons an hour. After a further 8 yards 7 different minerals were found and by this time the water flow had increased to 4200 gallons an hour. The first coal seam was reached at 16 yards below the surface. The water was eventually controlled by metal tubing, which has been described earlier. Eventually the total depth of 356 yards was reached, with no less than 132 different strata including many large and small coal seams. The main working coal being 'The Low Main', coal which measured some 5 feet 6 inches of good workable coal.

South Hetton Colliery:

This was one of the most expensive sinking in the county. The pit was situated 7 miles east of Durham. The quicksand and water being more formidable here than at any colliery. The pumping engine here was no less than 300 horsepower, and it happened to be the most powerful in the district. This engine was contained in a massive stone engine house which included three galleries and even to gaze at it was simply amazing.

Pemberton Pit (Near Sunderland):

The water here ran at 3000 gallons a minute. For the lifting of this water required a double acting Steam Engine with power of 200-horse power. This water had to be drained through an off-take drift. The large engine used for this, in the pit was indispensable. The first coal was not found until 1851 and at 344 feet below the surface. Again the cast metal tubing, which was proving worth their weight in gold, controlled the water.

Murton Colliery:

An important winning in the first half of the 19th. Century was at Murton Colliery. In order to sink these shafts the sinkers had to overcome many problems. Which they successfully did. In addition to having to bore through a considerable thickness of magnesium limestone that was full of water bearing fissures and infact some 417 feet thick, a sand bed occurred at the base of this formation, which was 28 feet thick. The total water flow was 9,306 gallons a minute, which was dealt with by 27 sets of lifting bucket pumps operating with steam supplied by 39 boilers. There were 3 shafts at this colliery, 2 being 14 feet in diameter and the third one being 16 feet. Sinking commenced in 1837 and it took 62 months before coal was found.

Apedale, North Staffordshire:
The deepest pit on record was Apedale, which was sunk to a depth of 2,145 ft. from the surface. The smallest shafts at this period were Somersetshire and Hampshire, where they ranged from 4ft.to 5ft. in diameter, while at Yorkshire they ranged from 8 ft. to 10 ft. and at Lancashire 12 ft shafts were used. In South Wales circular shafts around about 13 ft. was used. Oval shafts ranging from 16 ft. to 10 ft. also existed in Wales. The Polka Pit, in Durham, was thought to be the largest in diameter at this time which was 16 ft.

Marsdon Colliery:
In the north of England a very difficult sinking was at Marsdon. This pit was commenced in 1877, and took over 7 years to complete. The total water dealt with at the time was 11,612 gallons a minute, this was for both shafts. When the pumps couldn't clear the water anymore it was decided to copy the Kind Chaudron system of boring out the water under water, to do this the diameters of the shafts were reduced to 14 ft. and the sinking under this system proved a success, incidentally this system was first tried about 1850. Kind & Chaudren was the first persons to replace iron rods with wooden rods. The successes of this system was due to the wood being buoyant in the water, this allowing boring to greater depths.

Dawdon Colliery:
One of the largest coal owners of that time was the Sixth Marquis of Londonderry. It was the year 1899 and they were finding problems with Seaham Colliery, to such an extent they decided to sink a further shaft at Dawdon. This was very close to the North Sea. The experiences which they had at Seaham they also faced at Dawdon and also at Murton some years earlier. After penetrating a layer of sand the shaft was flooded with water, which flooded into the shaft at a tremendous rate, and it proved all too much for the pumps to clear. The sinkers at the time were exceptionally good at solving problems, especially when experiencing similar problems at Murton, where a freezing technique was used with success this also worked earlier still at Washington. On May 16th. 1902 the Theresa shaft reached a depth of 350 ft. The Castlereagh was also sunk that year. Work

Engineers and Mining experts who planned and sank local shafts in the Durham area in 1860. Below Shafsmen 1906:

Marsdon Colliery Sinkers

ceased for a period on the Theresa pit until the work on the Castlereagh caught up. By April 20th. 1903 both shafts were through the most dangerous phase of the sinking including the limestone, but then there was the water to consider. Both shafts at that time being handed over to a German company of Gerhard and Koenig of Northaven.

That certainly was not the end of the Dawdon saga, bore holes were drilled around the diameter of 30 feet and drilled to a depth of 484 ft. tubes were inserted with cooling agents, a mixture of Brine, Chloride of Magnesia and Ammonia. The mixture was re-cycled after being cooled by compressors at bank. A further obstacle was found in that as the tide rose and fell, the water in the shaft did likewise, this was due to the closeness of the sea, and it was slowing down the freezing process. They got over this by filling the lower Castlereagh shaft with 190 tons of cement which stopped the water flow. At long last the sinkers could blast their way through the frozen shaft. Everything about this operation was critical, the amount of explosive especially. Despite everything they completed the sinking by 6th. Sept.1907. Just one month before the sinking was completed 2 sinkers Henry Dun and George Attwood were killed. A huge power cable crashed down Castlereagh shaft.

The sinkers were slowly descending in a kibble at the time and the sheer velocity of the cable gave the men little chance of survival. This sad disaster wasn't the end of it for within a week a cradle collapsed in the same shaft killing three men Thomas Brown (25) his brother George Brown (23) and Robert Briggs (30). These men working in the shaft in a Kibble when a chain broke throwing the 3 men 200 ft. to their deaths. The Browns father who had been a Master Mason had died 2 months earlier widowing their mother, now having no money to support younger members of the Brown family, it was amazing that so much misery could be inflicted on one family. Such was the Trials and Tribulations of Sinkers at these times. The Castlereagh shaft was officially completed on Oct.5th. 1907, 'What a price to pay' before calculating the financial cost, the tragic deaths of 5 sinkers. Lord Londonderry extended the housing at Dawdon from 83 houses to 20 streets of houses. By 1910 3300 miners were producing one million tons of hand-hewed coal a year. Lord Londonderry built the population a church and the miners with deductions from their wages built a recreation centre and sports ground at Dawdon Dene,

Above Seaham Colliery

Above the New modern day Washery introduced to Dawdon Colliery in later years. The sea can be clearly seen in the background:

Above the 'Mill Inn', Seaham, Where the 'North of England Mechanical Engineers', first meetings took place. The Inn was also where the 1852 Explosion Inquest was held, also the site of the Election Riots in 1874, Below 'Seaham Hall', where Byron was married. Lord Londonderry also owned the Hall & gave it to the Seaham people as a Sanatorium:

THE HARD AND SAD YEARS

The years between 1750 and 1900, were hard and a lot of way's sad, for the men of the Mining Industry of the times. While coal owners were making vast profits, out of coal leading to vast fortunes, men were fighting and in some cases dying for a paltry existence for their families and themselves. Every penny earned had to be virtually fought for in such a way, that if the same conditions prevailed for the same wage in the present day, the present society just would not stand for it, and it would not need Trade Unions, to convince anyone regarding this. The early mining years were ripe with stories of victimisation, eviction, and tyranny, within their own ranks, men who blacklegged, probably because of starvation, on their own comrades, by working for ruthless coal-owners, making disputes for better conditions impossible, for men in dispute with their employers, who were locked out. There was constant fear of disgraceful behaviour, by Lay-Magistrates, and even fear of facing up to ex-comrades, who were now part of the Military, and where the fear of being shot by these on orders from rogue Magistrates, were very real. The early years of the industry were indeed repulsive.

Most early people leasing mines were speculators, people hell bent on making a quick profit. It was people such as this who expected men and boys to work long 16 hour shifts, in pits for virtually nothing, Boys at the tender age of 6 were expected to work 16 hours as trapper boys, opening and shutting doors, as coal was transported, (the great George Stephenson, was an un-educated trapper boy) in his younger years. Women also were expected to work down the pit, until such times as they married and had children. As early as 20th. Of August 1662 there is seen to be a need to combine with others in a body for strength, against ruthless coal owners, when 2000, miners signed a petition, to the King, asking for redress, against these people. One of the main concerns being, the proper ventilation, of the mines, explosions from gasses such as Fire-damp, then After-damp, were exceedingly more and more regular. The one shaft mines were used frequently, with the shaft divided with brattice, for up-cast and downcast air, with a fire furnace at the base, of the shaft, which was a constant danger, of triggering gasses, and firing coal dust, constantly in the air. The petition to the King was never sent, and all of the men who signed it were one way or another victimised cruelly, especially the instigators.

The men had the courage to again send in a petition, and this time the King and his Ministers started to take notice. Changes were ordered, for the better, especially with ventilation, and the eradication of gasses, such as firedamp, in 1676. But dangerous practices were still carried on, with the demands of still more and more inflated profits, from the coal owners, and the miners having to provide a living for themselves and their families, From time to time, terrible accidents undoubtedly happened, like North Biddick Pit, on the Wear, where 72 people, men boys, not forgetting woman, were violently, killed, by an explosion, of Fire-damp. A further explosion, from firedamp happened, at Lambton Colliery, on 22 August 1766, when 100 people died; a lamp that had been lowered down ignited the blast, the shaft for Masons to re-light the furnace, at the bottom of the shaft, which had been undergoing repairs. This caused a terrible explosion, which could be heard for 3 miles around. The explosion killed everything in its, path, shooting people away just like a cannon. Heads arms, and legs were found for weeks afterwards, and the ground at the surface was littered with timber, coal, and other litter for miles around. In 1805, another explosion happened at Hebburn, leaving 25 widows, and 81 children, without fathers, and husbands. The same time, an accident happened at Ox Close, Washington, which also left, 18 widows, and 70 children dependants. On the 25th. Of May 1812, at Felling Colliery, 92 work people died leaving, 41 widows, and 133 children to be cared for. This was the chilling start to the early coal industry. About 1650, about 7000, men were employed in the Newcastle Area, and approx., 10,000 men were employed in the Sea areas, such as Hartley, Blyth, and other sea pits, in this growth area ventilation would have to be seriously looked at.

The First Organised Protest

Around about 1810, many miners joined together, after a meeting at Long-Benton, went on strike, in a dispute with coal owners, regarding a binding agreement. With the help of some rogue Magistrates, the men were committed to Durham Prison, there were so many that the prison was full, and the overflow had to be held at the Bishop of Durham's stables, where Royal Carmarthenshire Militia guarded them by special Constables, and Durham Volunteers, and later; further daily arrests, were made until the Jail and stables could take no more.

For all too many years it had been passed on by families, to act reverently, to their betters, bowing before their Lords and Masters, men were beginning to rethink these principals. Mine owners, were starting to realise these facts, men were starting to think rationally, on matters of common-sense, and safety, and many highly intelligent individuals were starting to emerge, who could and would act as spokesmen, for these depressed people, on such matters as conditions, safety, and justice. In the Northern Coalfields the Northern miners won their case. The proposals, were agreed, by the coal owners, and has been the basis for agreement ever since, Called 'Binding Time' and is meant from the day the contract is made, in one year, until the same, next year, when the year of contract expires, and which was now dated 5th. Of April, and not in October, as the mine owners wanted to enforce. Around about 1800, because of a shortage of miners, mine owners paid out a bounty, so as to keep the men at the pit, this was also called Binding Money, £10-£20, was paid according to what individuals did, and they retained miners in this way. The miners found that they were tied to that particular pit, even if the job that they did was paid elsewhere at a higher rate. In most cases the miners spent the money in ale houses, then finding themselves tied to that pit, for a whole year, and the pit owners carried these contracts out to the letter.

The Great Strike, 1844

On 5th. April 1844. The miners of Durham and Northumberland terminated their agreement with the employers, the present agreement that had been agreed in 1843-4, but far from fair. The miners, refused to enter into a new agreement, until certain conditions had been re-negotiated and agreed. The owners refused to do this, resulting in a general strike, making all pits in Northumberland and Durham idle. The first general meeting was held at Shadows Hill, bands played, and flags, were waved and banners, carried. A wagon was placed strategically for a platform, and a mass of people waited in anticipation, for the start of the meeting, infact nearly, 40,000 people stood there, that chilly spring morning, woman with babies in their arms, old men with walking sticks, young men, for a change out of their working clothes, meeting people that they had never seen for years, because of the long hours that was a way of life. In the mining communities. All, both young old, men and woman, determined to strike out for their rights, to have a decent way of life. In a way it was like a holiday atmosphere, all waiting for the first speakers, where, with the strength of unity something could at-last be done about working conditions at coal mines, in the North of England.

Mr. Mark Dent as chairman opened the meeting, addressing, the men as *"fellow men" "We have long been divided, but I hope this day it will be the uniting of the miners of the Tees, Wear and Tyne," "for the purpose of, having our grievances adjusted for they are manifold severe," "we have longed for re-dress," "we have been treated with scorn," "but now we are resolved to be free," "we are, an insulted, oppressed, and de-graded, body of men," "if the masters had made anything like reasonable proposals, we would of accepted them," "but they have put forward a miserable, proposition," "an infamous bond under which, many men have been working for a pittance." "But we will do so no longer,"* he went on to say, that he hoped that reasoning would take place, instead of strikes, between master and men, and that men should get a fair days pay for a fair days

130

work. *Men are a class that are not looked on with respect, from most of the public, and the general press, were against them.*

"Our employers use every means to oppress us," "but now, that there is understanding among us," "are we any longer to drag the chains, of slavery," "to bear the yokes of bondage, and toil," "in the bowels of the earth as we have done"? Mr George Charlton was called on to move the first resolution, and he made a similar speech, saying that the miners had been insulted, ill treated and looked upon with scorn and contempt. Just prior to finishing his speech, he moved the following resolution, 'That it being the lawful and inherent right,' 'of every working man, in the kingdom, to obtain the best price for his labour,' 'this meeting avows its intention, and determination, to procure, individuality and collectively, a better remuneration, for their labour, than has here to fore, been paid,' 'and to abstain from working until such rumination be obtained'. Mr Robert Archer seconded the resolution, saying 'that they had now stepped into liberty, they had long been shackled, and chained,' 'and had acted against,' 'instead of for each other,' 'because they had not been united'. He finished his speech by saying, 'they had no ill will against, nor did they wish to injure, the coal owners, ' 'all they wished to do,' 'was to be paid for their labour, and that it was just, and right'. The Chairman then put the resolution to the meeting which was easily carried. The following resolutions were put forward and again carried, without hesitation,

By Mr. John Tulip, Mr. Edward Richardson, and Mr. Thomas Pratt. *That this meeting is of the opinion that the bonds, proposed by the masters, are of such a nature, as to be injurious to our welfare. That the drivers and Trappers, should only work 10 hours, also the suspension of heavier tubs and Shetland ponies, which did not have the temperament, for underground work:* (a driver had recently been killed by working with larger tubs) *That the coal owners of the district, having refused, to meet a deputation of the workmen, to arrange to discuss, the differences, existing between miners and coal owners. This meeting announces, that such a deputation is still waiting on them in order to settle such matters, so as to prevent, any continued, cessation, of labour, providing the said coal owners avow, their intention to meet for such a purpose.* This resolution was seconded by Mr. William Daniel's (editor of the miners advocate) he begged the men to never use violence, and this would give them moral power, and a shield of defence.

Mr. Richardson, said that, Mr. Joseph Pease, the mild, Quaker and Liberal Politician, he who had told the woman of Barnard Castle, that he would obtain cheap sugar and tea for them, and would 'watch the tap', and who when he got to parliament voted 20 millions of money, as compensation, to the slave holders. This friend wanted Waggoner's, masons, and joiners, to go down and hew coal, for him. But Joseph was deceived, these men would not go down and they all joined the union. The crowd cheered loudly, then the chairman addressed the meeting, saying if they if they lost the battle, they would fight them again, 'they would stand by their union, & still return to the combat,' 'let them never despond, for right would overcome might, if they stand true to each other'. 'At the present time, the miners had a small house with one room, with 7 children to bring up, with a small pantry in which to keep provisions, a sitting room, 1 bedroom, this was the miners castle,' ' the employers not even supplying education, for the children.' 'It was a disgrace to the owners and a credit to the men to manage on these terms,' 'In all ages, Tyranny, could only exist, so long & it was in this case,' 'the good times were coming. After a vote of thanks, to the Chairman, and 3 cheers for the union, the giant crowd broke up, in a peaceful manner.

As said in a early chapter, men, were starting to emerge from rank and file, that would greatly advance the power of the union, they would act as spokesmen, organisers, and as rational thinkers, assist the miners in their rights, against ruthless coal owners. The following is a small synopsis, regarding 3 of these people;

Doctor John Wilson

John Wilson was born at Greatham, in the year 1837, after leaving school he worked in a Weardale Quarry. He later found work at Ludworth, Littletown, Sherburn Hill, and Lady Seaham Collieries. Wilson went to sea, around about 1860, and then returned to mining, at Sherburn Hill pit, where he became secretary until the owners broke contact with the union. In 1864, he went to America with his wife, on his return he formed a union lodge at Haswell, but the owners refused to bind him. Wilson formed a lodge at Wheatley Hill, and it was here that he was elected to the DMA. Council. After the Colliery was sold, the new owners did not employ Wilson, so he used this period, to take the job as organiser, to the miners National Union in the midlands. He became DMA. Treasurer succeeding, Nicholas Wilkinson, in 1882. John Wilson was very well thought of in union circles, when Paterson died he became General Secretary, in 1895. In 1910, Durham University bestowed on him, an Honouree Degree of Doctor, of Civil Law, and after this he was always known as Doctor Wilson. Wilson met Gladstone in 1884, regarding union reform, and he was a Liberal MP representing Houghton-le-Spring. He was actually nominated by Sir Joseph Whitwell Pease, in 1890, and elected that year in the Houghton-Le-Spring seat. John Wilson died, in 1915, leaving a legacy, to the DMA, of a membership at the time of 141,947 members.

William Hammond Patterson

Patterson was born at Fawdon Square, Newcastle, in 1847; he was the son of a quarry worker. His stepmother sent him to work at Jesmond Quarry, at 11 years of age, but within the year he started work at, Heworth Colliery. Patterson was elected secretary of Heworth Lodge, in 1865, and attended the meeting at Thornley, in 1869, as delegate from Heworth; he worked on the Committee of the union, when the union was in its infancy in 1870. In June the same year, he was elected organiser for the South West Durham District, and together with crake carrying, Tommy Ramsey, recruited many members, for the DMA. After Crawford's death in 1890, he was elected corresponding secretary, this was a difficult period, after the strike of 1892. Patterson like Crawford was a Primitive Methodist, and also a close friend of radical, Joseph Cowen, (the great supporter of Revolutionary and Liberation Movements). Paterson finally died in 1896

Tommy Ramsey

Tommy Ramsey had been active in Judes Union in 1844; he was a leading advocate for the movement. After participating in the famous Thornley meeting he was blacklisted, and after which he worked hard in the Colliery areas as an agent, to recruit members for the DMA.

Tommy was a white haired man, who carried his wooden crake, everywhere, using his Tyneside dialect to effect, when canvassing more members for the movement. Tommy's work was dangerous to say the least, he slept in hedgerows, fields and barns, no one dared help him in-case they were evicted from their homes. On one occasion, he was badly beaten by a man in the pay of coal owners, who also burnt his crake. This did not deter Tommy who came on even stronger, got himself another crake and continued on, even better than before. At the 1872, Durham Gala, on seeing the vast crowds on the race course, he remarked, "Now let thy servant die in peace," "For mine eyes have seen thy salvation," Later Tommy had a fall, at his brother's house, in Blaydon, where he passed away on 8th. Of May 1873.

The Continuation & Sad Outcome of the Strike

The miners in general were very determined, to see this strike out to its bitter end, even though they knew that it would cause many heart aches and starvation amongst the mining communities. One thing that was noted was the miners wives were very determined to see it out to its conclusion and they were 100% behind their partners, in a hope of at least getting a liveable wage and better conditions, for a bitterly depressed group of people, who daily risked life and limb, for coal owners, working unsociable hours for a pittance. Every pit arranged themselves into committee's mainly to raise funds, they pledged themselves to always act in peace, and regular meetings were held throughout Durham and Northumberland, in order to measure progress. The coal owners put out a statement that, miners could earn 35/8d a day, which was dis-credited by the miners, because it was generally known that, the best hewers in the best seams could only make at the most, 2/6, to 2/10, a day, and work was not available every day as other trades did. It had infact been proved that after taking off money for fines, doctors, coals, picks, etc. an average miner, earned an average of 11 shilling a week. It was further said by the coal owners that they could not afford any improvement in wages because of the depression in the coal trade, but this was also disproved, in that the London Market there was only, 6d a ton difference, in coal prices in 1831, as to the present day.

By now all businesses were feeling the knock on effect of the strike, and a lot of businesses that relied on the miner's money were really feeling the pinch and going out of business. The coal owners after seeing that the miners were very determined, started to recruit blackleg labour, and agents were sent out around the Country especially in Wales, looking for such people offering them many incentives. On the arrival of the blacklegs problems were caused with housing them, and because they had no hold on the houses the striking miners were evicted, one by one, piling up their furniture roughly, away from the houses without any care at all. The miners had promised not to use violence certainly had their patience tested.

The bailiffs on entering the house first saying, 'Will you Work', on the reply of 'No', they started to take roughly every possession from the house. This started much yelling, and shouting, wives and children were bitterly crying, children's treasured crudely made wooden toys, pulled apart roughly, wives few personnel effects, which may have been passed down to them for years, roughly thrown into the street, all of the crying did not have any effect on these inhuman people, who were in the pay of the coal owners. For years it was always known that most bailiffs, were recruited from very unpleasant and hard hearted people, but these were the scourge of the earth, taking away from a very de-pressed people, probably the only little security they had, in their homes and pitiful belongings fully sanctioned by the coal owners, and rogue magistrates. The Magistrates not daring to appose the owners, resulting in justice not being administered, as it should of been. Men started to use their furniture and other materials, to make makeshift homes, which were quite habitual, infact between Seghill, and Seaton Delaval, a complete village took shape, with chests of drawers, desks, beds, the roof of which was covered by canvas, or even bedding. A mainly happy atmosphere most times prevailed, once it had been accepted that, they had lost their homes, they managed to make the best of it. One consolation being the weather was good, and the summer evenings were quite pleasant, sitting talking about things that previously they had not had time to talk about. The odd fiddle and mouth organ or even, a penny whistle appeared, and by this time miners had learned the art of making home brew, which made, the moment better. One thing that was sure they could go no lower, the woman came up with, cost saving nutritious food, especially, with rabbits, and game, (partridge, pheasant), local poachers having a field day, salmon and rainbow trout miraculously, appearing. One thing that they all had in common was hope, their trade was coal and this was the main power of the Country, and the blacklegs could not supply the demand at the time, it was hoped that the owners would have to concede sooner or later.

The turning out of striking families went on, pregnant woman, bed-ridden men, who were sick, innocent babies in their crudely made cradles, the aged, feeble, turned out of homes that they had lived in all of their lives, including childhood. Every one of the miners were roughly, and harshly treated, furniture was smashed to pieces, household goods which had been treasured, along with food, thrown into the road, for all of this the miners tempers held, as promised. There is not enough pages in this book, to describe the atrocities, that were carried out against the miners and their families, for practising their only right of withdrawing their labour, until such times as they were given a living wage, and better conditions. After all these men were risking their lives on a daily basis, to make the coal owners, rich men.

Meetings were held throughout the area, just to report on progress, at one such meeting a troop of 6th. Dragoons, with Mr. R.S. Surtees, at the head of them, demanded to see the chairman, obviously carrying out an act of re-oppression, showing the miners what would happen if they got anyway out of line. There were other reports of Sabre's being drawn, and the issue of pistols to people who used them to threaten miners, was rife. The Coal owners introduced into the pit villages, lawless vagabonds, whom they had recruited, from towns throughout the country, with promises of high bounties, but who were proved useless, in the pits. The miners were a special kind of people doing a special kind of work, who were bred into this trade, and were even evolving body wise, to cope, with the pressures and hard work, most miners doing low face work, in mostly 18 inch seams were small framed men, muscled where they required the power in their arms and shoulders and their calf mussels, to enable them to push tubs. More and more miner's cottages stood empty, as the families were forced to live rough. This is what the owners resorted to, to damage the miners for striking. The owners tried everything to break the strike, inducing the weaker members of the union to break rank by offering them bribes, they gave notice to shopkeepers that if they supplied the miners with any provisions, then they would forfeit their shops and all of the stock, therein. Lord Londonderry went down in history for a similar action, after which it was alleged that he regretted.

He sent a letter out to the Seaham shopkeepers on 20th. July 1844 that if they supplied any of the striking families, they would be marked men and all of the estate business would be moved to Newcastle not forgetting that he owned the shops anyway. Radcliffe Colliery, in the north brought in 32 Cornish miners, who were engaged on contract for a year, at 4 shilling a day, according to their merits. On their first payday, they received 3 shilling, the next week, 2/4d, the third week, 2/6d, the consequences of this was a withdrawal of their labour, for 2 days and they used very abusive Cornish language. If they had been the regular miners they would have been put in prison. Finally the owners to save face gave them the 4 shilling as promised, which was a great loss to the owners, as the Cornish men could not match the Durham miners and they could not hew above 4 tubs of coal a day, when the Durham men could treble that amount and even more. This apparently cost Radcliff Colliery, £90 each fortnight, and yet they would not settle the measly demands of the miners. After awhile the Cornish men absconded, and the mine owner put out a reward, for their capture, which was £50. Newcastle police caught 4 of the men and brought them to Amble in gigs, with a posse of police, where they were kept prisoner from, Monday night until Wednesday morning.

The Cornishmen attempted to escape and this threw Amble into a panic. Police and special constables, followed by, pit Overmen, and banks men, were running everywhere, through cornfields and rivers. The Cornish miners were finally captured, and brought back to Amble, in a steam boat, where they were brought before Magistrates, at a special justices court. The Cornish men were represented by, Mr. Busby, (solicitor). A ruling came in favour of the men much to the delight of the Durham miners, after all of the chasing here and there the owners had to pay the costs of the hearing, with the police work also, this together with the reward money. These were the devious ways the coal owners did to break the strike, it was generally, known that North East miners were the best in the world, even the sinkers were consulted many times throughout the country and even Europe, if there was any sinking problems or indeed any mining problems. Large numbers of men started arriving from Wales, it seamed ironic that they would blackleg, on the North East miners, but they did, my own mother, disliked Welshmen all of her life, simply because of the way they worked in the pits while men were on strike, and this dis-like was past on through the years. At the time of this strike policemen protected the Welshmen, but they need not of worried on that score as The North East miners had promised a peaceful strike and they had carried this out to the letter. To be fair on occasions, the Welshmen said that they had been misled, and they said they did not know that the men were on strike. and they said that if they had enough money they would go back to Wales. The miners gave them money that they could not afford, and it was proved in many cases that, they just returned to the mine owners getting a higher bounty than they got before, so they were being paid by both masters and men and this was proved on many occasions. Many men on strike went to other parts of the country, some stayed with relatives while collecting funds for their cause, their relatives being employed in other industries. Some young men even leaving the industry and finding work elsewhere, some even trying their luck in America, or even farther field, this was a great loss to the coal industry as these were strong experienced miners, and the industry could not do without men such as these in a growing industry, as coal mining.

The owners eventually found enough men, to get a steady flow of coal from their pits. The strike was now in its 18th. Week, and sadly there was innocent breakaway from the rank and file. Many collieries refused to accept many of the men back. The families were now at starvation point, and unable to endure the miseries of going without food any longer, some were ill, and the children were too weak to beat the mildest of colds, and their immune systems were very weak, they were still camping out and by now, the cold winds and rain were starting to get the better of them. Rumours were rife that the union had broken up, but this was not the case, but the families were so hungry they were starting not to care.

The Durham miners were the first to give way, the Northumberland men still standing firm, it was known that the Durham miners had suffered far more hardship, than the Northumbrian's who were still resolute. It was decided to hold a general meeting, at Newcastle Town Moor, on the 13th. August, 1844 and the Durham miners holding a similar meeting at the Sands Durham, where 10,000, people attended. Similar Resolutions were carried at both meetings, with the same object in mind to strengthen the resolve of the men, the general wording also being similar.

'That after standing 18 weeks, and seeing the base and unmanly conduct, of our masters, who have by promises, threats and intimidation, succeeded in getting a number of men to work to suit their present purpose, and thereby entailing misery, on present and future generations. To prevent this direful calamity, this meeting therefore calls upon, such as they have been deluded, by false promises of the masters,, to join the ranks of the Association. 'That in the opinion of this meeting, the miners of the district, ought to be very guarded against reports emanating, from the parties in the guise of Ministers of the Gospel, persuading the men to go back to work, by painting our position in false colours. This meeting pledges, itself not to believe any report unless it bears the stamp of authority, from our Association. Mr. Christopher Haswell moved the 3rd. resolution, that the meeting pledges itself to stand by the Association, and to continue united until such times as we have obtained our rights', 'thanks having been voted to the Chairman, and to Sir, John Fife, for the use of the ground for the meeting',

The meeting broke up in an orderly fashion; the same procedure was also carried at Durham. These were shows of solidarity by the miners who were clearly loosing this fight. It was further resolved, from the Newcastle miners to send 2 men to the Durham and Wearside areas, to encourage them to stand fast, and to stay away from the Tyneside areas, but hundreds of men, some starving, made their way to Tyneside collieries, and obtained work wherever they could find it. This was the position of the 1844 strike, it would live with the miners, and their families the rest of their lives, the determination of the men to fight for their rights was never matched, but now this was the end, and they had lost, and were compelled to return to work, on the terms of the masters. The miners and their union, were victims of oppression, by owners such as Lord Londonderry, the miners gave way to immense wealth, and also the never ending worry of their wives and little one's. Their families were on the poverty line, with no homes.

The men were driven back to their holes in the earth, and at the time absolute slavery. There would be other days, as the union got stronger, public opinion may next time may be on the side of the miner. One thing was for certain there would be very astute representation, from very clever, loyal Trade union officials who would be hell bent on improving standards, and wages for these hard working people. Although the miners lost the strike, the overall loss to the owners ,was enormous, and it would of been better if the owners had paid the meagre amount asked for in the first place. Now was the time of reckoning, for the blacklegs, and others and there was an air of bitterness, felt by the miners, on the 11th. Of August,1844 a Brakeman was shot dead, he worked at Ravensworth, at the time he was in the company of a watcher, a man called Jefferson, the Brakeman was called, Thomas Robson, he was shot in a field and the culprit was never found.

Aftermath:

Welshman, and blacklegs occupied double Row in Seaton Delaval at the time. One night two of the Welshmen went to the Hastings Arms, which at the time was run by Mr. Bell, they went with a stone bottle (grey hen) to get it filled with beer. Two Northumberland Pitman were in the bar, and a fight broke out. In the space of ten minutes, hundreds of men came together, English, Irish, and Welsh, and a pitched battle took place. They armed themselves, with anything they could lay their hands on, Garden Railings, Pick Shafts. The fighting spread to all parts of Seaton Delaval, and men were being badly injured. Mr Atkinson the under Viewer, at Seaton Delaval, tried to make the peace, he owned a Cocker Spaniel, which, when Atkinson went into the crowd followed him, the dog was pinned to the ground with a pick which went right through it. Mr Atkinson went to get the army who were billeted, close by, but the Commander would not commit his men until a Magistrate had read out the riot act. Before a Magistrate could be found the Welshmen began to yield, finally fleeing in numbers, back to their homes as fast as they could.

The Englishmen would certainly of followed them, possibly killing them and possibly burning their houses, but it was rumoured that the army was arriving. The truth of the matter was that there were badly injured men on both sides, but the Welshmen coming off worse. In the following days some of the culprits were arrested during the night, and made an example of, they were handcuffed and thrown into carts, and paraded through the villages. Rioting spread throughout the mining areas, the owners of pits leaving the Welshmen and other blacklegs to face up to the angry miners, on their own. Not only the Welshmen were effected by this but it also effected their families and especially sons who had just started down the mines, working as putters drivers etc.; these innocent lads were made to pay a high price for their fathers involvement in blacklegging. The Welshmen had no peace at all; other miners would not ascend or descend, in the same cage in the pit with them. In shops or pubs they would not stand or sit anywhere near them. Eventually they started leaving the area in large numbers. Some Welshman refused to leave, and one man actually worked at Seaton Delaval for 20 years, but even in that time his company was never tolerated. This brings to an end all I wished to record, about this sad period in 'Mining History', better times would eventually come, after further disputes, they would eventually be paid a higher wage than any other, manual worker in England, and the public would recognise them for what they were. Hard working conscientious men, deserving a fair and just wage, and the same conditions for working daily in the bowels of the earth:

Murton Collery men on strike digging for coal in an old tip; below Later in the Century Nationalisation meeting also at Murton

From Witton Park to Shropshire

K en Robinson's parents were Gordon and Edith Robinson; his father was born in 1898 at Low Thompson Street, Witton Park, Bishop Auckland, Co. Durham. Other family at this time consisted of three sisters and twin brothers the twins dying at the time of the Influenza epidemic in 1918. The Robinson's family originated from North Yorkshire. Kens mothers maiden name was 'Tarn', she was born in Howden le Wear; a village three miles north of Witton Park. She had three sisters & two brothers. The family moved from Teesdale years previously. Kens Grandmothers maiden name being 'Bennington'.Gordon Robinson a miner and this was his chosen

Marshall Green Pit, Witton le Wear, L/R Tom Hutchinson, Gordon Robinson , Sid. Raine son and Bill Raine Father:

profession Mother and father were married at the 'Methodist Chapel', in Bridge Street, Howden le Wear. Ken was born on the 15th. November 1925 at Witton Park. At this time home was 35, Black Road, Witton Park. Ken was the third child, Olive, was born 1922, Gordon November 1924, Ronnie in September 1937. Father worked at the local Colliery when he was not unemployed. Witton Park very unlike the sound of the village was an absolute slum of the worst kind. Streets that had not been completed, gas lighting occasionally flickered on and off; water was available but electricity just did not exist. Houses were literally thrown up, mainly to accommodate Iron workers & colliery workers and were situated in depressing narrow streets. There was an abundance of pubs and chapels. Ken recollected people using some of the pubs also the Baptist, Methodist and Catholic Churches but how the other premises survived was a complete mystery.

Number 35, Black Road where Ken was born was a typical village house with a leaking roof; rising damp was evident along with badly fitting windows; no electric or hot water. An earth toilet stood in the yard and a cold-water tap was situated behind the door and a tin bath hung ominously on a nail on the house wall. The bath-tin was often used by the fire in the kitchen by whoever had just finished a shift at the pit. The area had no vehicle access to the rear of the houses and the earth toilets had to be emptied into an old bath tin and carried to a horse drawn 'Coupe Cart'. Old Tom Gillett had the contract; he owned a small farm at East Park. Mr Gillett employed a young man called Hall who's duty it was to carry the tin bath past the doors to the cart. The smell from it was overbearing especially in summer time. Flies were everywhere; cockroaches and black clocks were part of everyday life. Mother still managed to keep the house neat and tidy thus providing a little home comfort. The residents of the area were mainly good people. A short distance from the house was pleasant walks along wonderful riverbanks; one consolation in the depressed state of the housing was that our particular house being an end terrace, had garden front and rear and the views lifted the spirits.

In the 1930s some Councillors who claimed to be educated thought that the village required to be changed. Some unemployed men were put to work levelling the 'Old Jane Pit' heaps. They were paid nine pence each day & given a pair of working boots. The Council made sure that the men did not get rich by restricting the work to two days each week. Later two swings were erected with a roundabout and see-saw. They then decided to make it into a football field but grass would not grow and there were no goal posts. The area was re-named Recreation Ground. There was no money left for any other change. The Council had other bright ideas when they decided to change the street names. Black Road became 'Park Road', 'Jane Pit Row', became 'Park Terrace'. The houses still had their problems of leaking roofs, rising damp, bad fitting doors and windows, no electric or hot water. The earth toilet buckets still had to be carried away yet addresses gave the impression of living in luxury, near a wonderful park.

In 1930 the Depression started to bite hard after the 1926 strike when the miners had been locked out for six months. The savings that hard working people had scraped to put by, for emergencies was now long gone on lifesaving food. In Bishop Auckland area 52% of available males were unemployed and this was much higher than other parts of Bishop Auckland females were not even considered for the majority of employment. In the Witton Park area the averages were far below this.

This was the year that Ken started school. He vividly remembered uncaring and the cold welcome from teachers based in a corrugated roofed

Father Gordon Robinson

iron building that was hard to keep warm. Two schools were situated in the village 'The Council School', & 'St. Chad's', which was the Roman Catholic School. At the Council school we used slates and slate pencils. These were used until we were able to write; apparently paper was just too expensive to use initially at Witton. As previously mentioned finance was sadly very short at our village because of the Depression. clothing was just inadequate. In extreme conditions; children shivered with the cold their diet not able to protect them against cold winds and severe weather. Some kids called at the 'Salvation Army', Hall to get a little food in their bellies, this was a mug of cocoa and a thick slice of bread and jam. Sometimes the kids lingered beside coke fuelled stoves for warmth and were late for school not wanting to face up to the cold weather once more. Savage uncaring teachers caned the kids for being late, four of the best warming their hands as well as their bellies.

When kids were about eleven years old there was an annual camp for a selected few. In 1937 my brother Gordon was picked. I had the double bed all to myself for once in my life. Ron was born in 1937 and from then on he was my bed companion. School dinners were not available in them days however some who were thought to be under nourished were given a glass of milk and two biscuits if after a medical this was found to be the case. Ken never qualified Olive and Gordon received this concession and if any child on this scheme were ever off school I got it instead. It was

Ken Robinson sitting to the right of Mr. Ernest Preston (Headmaster); Ken had a high regard for him who always wore ancle spats. Others to note, Tom Smith, Jim Chadwick, Joe Newton, Dick McGregor, Ernie Walton, Des Newton, Stan Thexton, John Gray, Ken & Headmaster, Fred Raine, Stan Dixon Joe Grady, John Graham. This was the 'Gardening Class', in the spring of 1939, at Witton Park school.

strange both Olive & Gordon were both fed on the same diet as I at home. The year was now 1939 my final school year this was the very year that I qualified for the camp. I had saved all of my coppers for the event and had the grand total of 3/9. On the Sunday before leaving, War was declared; earlier all had been issued with ID. Cards, & Gas masks. Every home received various types of blackouts for windows. We still went off to camp on the Monday, first of all calling at school with soap, towel, clean shirt, socks all in a paper bag with my 3/9 tucked deep into my pocket. On arrival we were told that due to the war the trip was now cancelled. We were told to return home with our things beautifully packed and return to school at dinnertime.

The war commenced, street lighting that did not count for much prior to the war disappeared all together, never to be lit again until after the war. Previously we had watched the lamp lighter Mr. Winter at the same time nightly, he light every lamp individually. All house windows were darkened and curtains closed before any light was turned on, these blinds had to be purchased by families, vehicles headlights were dimmed. Food rationing was introduced this made little difference to us or the rest of the population as we were rationed all of our lives.

In late 1938 to early 1939 my father was unemployed. He finally managed to get a job at 'Hole in The Wall Colliery'. Based at Crook he travelled to work on a bicycle. My memories living at 'Witton Park', were vivid prior to leaving school these were happy memories of playing near to the river & East Park', the 'Gill Fields', bird nesting in the meadows trees and river banks, sneaking into 'Kennel Wood', for blackberries; in the winter we had pleasant memories of sledging and making slides. While on my own I visited the old blacksmith's shop. This was up the Baltic & where I watched old Walter Blackett in amazement shoeing horses and completing other Smith's work. Although having his business at the Baltic he lived quite near to us. His work fascinated me, sparks were everywhere and the smell of the horse's hooves when fitting the new shoes lingered in the air. I made friends with him and he once made me runners for my sledge and also a booler & hook.

Typical Bath Tin:

Life at Witton Park was mainly pleasant and the high lights at that time was the 'Carnival Weekend' later came the Chapel trip to the Sea Side. Dad never missed our yearly trips to 'Durham Gala'. One of my mother's brothers Jim, worked at 'Blackhall Colliery'. We always met up with him at the Gala. New years eve, was another, exciting period in our lives; we all sat waiting for the 'first foot', who for years was Sid Thexton. The adults discussed the old year and hoped that the New Year would improve things.

On leaving school memories at the school was not all doom & gloom I still had many pleasant memories. My parents had always provided for us I was never over fed but at the same time never hungry. We had boots to wear, nice clean clothing on our backs nothing fancy but neat tidy and warm. Dad cobbled our boots, cut our hair; this experience was never forgotten. After the experience he ran our heads under the cold-water taps saying that it would stop us from getting cold in the head. On Friday nights there was always a cup of 'Senna Tea' this to keep the bowels open. Dad had many funny ideas for our well being; when he worked at 'Railey Fell Pit'; the pay office was at Ramshaw four miles away. On some Friday afternoons I had to go and collect his pay. We all had to help in the garden and during the winter nights helped mam make the clippie mats. Every night we had to clean our boots ready for school the following morning so even before we were adults we were conditioned for work. Another amazing event at this time was Sunday mornings when I was about twelve years old, one Sunday morning, Ron was just about crawling. We had a gate between the kitchen and where the tap was. I had the jug in my hand and jumped over the gate, I slipped on the jug and gashed my right knee. When Doctor Gama arrived Billy Blackett and father held me while he stitched the wound, no aesthetic at all; not a great morning.

On getting older in a lot of ways I felt that the Education system had failed in a great deal of ways. Many hours were wasted on learning ancient History of King Harold and 1066; important periods in the 'North of England', like the 'S&D Railways, Witton Park Ironworks', and our association with the iron masters 'Bolckow & Vaughan, the importance of the 1926 strike, the Depression, 'Trade Unions ', why we had two minutes silence Armistice day; why the war started in the first place. I would have enjoyed this History immensely. Mr. Ernest Preston our Head Master told us that the best thing we could do was to start reading; even if it was only a comic it would in some way stimulate the mind leading to other things I always felt that this was sound advice.

My first job was on a farm at Toft Hill. I survived on 7/6 a week including my keep. My working day commenced at 6am. Feed the horses, half a dozen pigs hand milk five cows before breakfast. The stock always came first even before the day began; for the 7/6 I worked eighty hours. Finally one night I had to stay up all night playing midwife to a 'Sow Pig'. After a few weeks I felt I had to change my occupation and it was goodbye farming and 'hello mining'. I had an open mind and mining was the start of a learning process for me. My education began in earnest due to the war mining jobs were plentiful. Most other older lads 'Contrary to views', were either called up or joined up, mainly to get away from the pits and the slavery of Mining. Later the Government due to the shortage of Miners on the home front classed mining as an exempt occupation later introducing

146

Bevan Boys. This was aimed at preventing men from leaving the industry. At this time it was crucial to keep coal fuel and as such power flowing from the Collieries mainly to feed the factories supplying arms for the allied forces and to produce coal for the home front. I left the farm on the Friday and started at the pit on the Monday.

My first pit was 'Marshall Green Colliery' the hours were 7am-3pm. I was a pony driver this job and Galloway putters prepared their horses before the shift began. They also had to be hosed down at the end of the

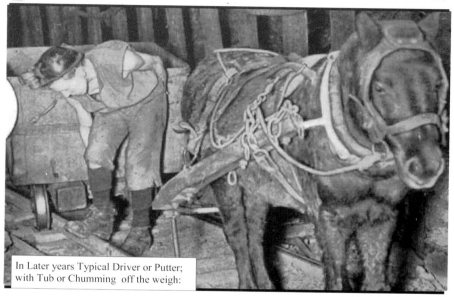

In Later years Typical Driver or Putter; with Tub or Chumming off the weigh:

shift; this was without extra pay and the shift worked out longer than the eight hours. The Saturday shift was from 5am until 11.30 am. The pay for lads under fifteen was 18/9 each week and as this was a naked light pit we had to supply our own lamps. The pit was roughly 2 ½. Miles from home so Gordon and I walked the distance together. My pay at least had risen from 7/6 to 18/9. That Monday morning I was sure this industry was where I belonged. The time listening to my father and uncle discussing the work became now a reality and I felt that I was continuing a family tradition. I sharp found out that childhood conversations dreams and reality were very different. There was no training, I was told to yoke the horse and your mate will show you the ropes.

My job as driver meant that I had to take Chumming's from Flat A to

147

These are a group of young miners near to the Jane Pit about 1900; depicts the hard and sad period when Ken started as a miner. The Jane Pit closed in April 1925 losing 255 jobs; which the village could ill afford. Below Miners from Railey Fell Colliery; between Toft Hill & Witton Park taken 1930 among others Thomas & George Wright, these were more mature miners but would be working tremendously hard for their living. Hard hats were not compulsory at this time. The men below were wearing pit hoggars (shorts). Most would have black coal related scars through having accidents:

Flat B. on arriving at Flat B. I would take full tubs out-bye. It all sounds simple but this certainly was not the case; the roadways were only 4ft. 6in. high and about 5 feet wide. There was not much room to drive the pony and we sat on the 'limbers', this meant sat between the horses backside and the tub being pulled. It was however very risky business. All Pit ponies were geldings or stallions. As it cost a lot of money to castrate them most

Witton Park about 1860

happened to be stallions. If one can imagine frustration in confined places with a horse not being gelded "What Joy" It was a daily battle of wits and will. In 'Bord & Pillar workings the driver and pony were last in the pecking order. Hewers and Putters were on piecework so they depended on the drivers getting the empties in, and full tubs out. Piece workers were not happy men if you failed them. I almost forgot most pits in South West Durham were wet pits. At the time no Pit Head bath's existed in this area so we walked home wet. This was a great pleasure in the winter (*Our bodies were shivering before arriving home*). The union eventually got payment 10 pence a day for over eighteens and 5 pence a day for anyone under eighteen. I could never understand how water could tell the difference. There was another important happening in my life that morning this happened to be the day I joined the 'NUM. Union'. I remained a member all of my working life. I played an active part ever since. My daughter and Partner are also active members of a leading 'Trade Union'.

I was very conscious of my first job at the pit just prior to leaving school a village young lad a few years older than I had been killed while riding on the Limbers; I had not been working long when one of my class

To Mr E Craggs
Hole in the Wall Colliery.   June 19th 1942

Dear sir,   (No 1)
          I hearby tender for and on behalf of R Lowery
G Robinson G Davidson N, Middlemiss for the two
West bargains up to let No 1 to be driven 6 feet high
and 6 feet wide stones to be kibbled and stowed in the
workings Old packs to be pulled out and renewed plus
timbering to be included in price. Price to be 16/- per yard
plus % additions any extra width required by the manager
to be paid in proportion.
                    (No 2.)
Curve to drive to connect up with No1 bargain 6 feet high
and 7 feet wide, stones to be kibbled and stowed in workings.
Price to be 17/- per yard plus % additions, coal hewing and
coal yard work to be paid at seam prices. Any stowing over
fifty yards from working face too heavy for one man or any
unreasonable distance away extra help to be found by
Manager Timbering included in price. Extra width to
be paid in proportion.

Old Mr. Robinson's bargain tender at the Colliery; Sheer slavery

STAINDROP FIELD HOUSE DRIFT MINE.

BUSTY SEAM L.A. 1652. 19th. August 1955.

PNEUMATIC PICK HEWING.

(1) Hewers shall be responsible for all work associated with the winning of coal from the places and doing any necessary stonework in the places.

(2) Hewers shall be responsible for the setting of all supports to comply with The Coal Mines Act and Support Rules as specified by the Manager under this Act.

(3) Men shall draw their own Explosives from the magazine and carry them into the pit and shall return unused explosives and empty canisters to the magazine at the end of the shift in accordance with the Explosives in Mines Order.

(4) The coal shall be filled as clean as possible.

(5) If the men are brought out of their working place they shall be paid according to the County Datal Rate agreement or if sent to work for which piece work rates are already fixed, they shall be paid at the applicable piecework rate.

(6) Men shall be responsible for the care of all gear issued by the management, and they shall carry in oil for picks and drills, and maintain the picks and drills in good condition.

(7) The prices to be paid for work under the foregoing conditions shall be :-

Prices amended	2 Tons	-	38/6
2nd. June 1959.	2½ "	-	42/-
	3 "	-	44/6
	3½ "	-	47/-
	4 "	-	50/-
	4½ "	-	53/6
	5 "	-	57/-

plus 3/9 per shift for each extra ½ Ton per shift.

Between tonnages on the above scale shall be paid pro rata to the nearest ¼ Ton.

This is an inclusive price, including the 4/11 per shift Flat Rate, and no other payments shall be made except payment as required by the County Wet Agreement and the Charlesworth Steel Award.

The shift rate is a gross rate and no percentage rates shall be paid on it.

(8) The shift rate shall be established on a weekly basis by dividing the total tonnage of the set for the week by the total number of shifts worked by the set.

(9) This agreement applies only to cavilled coal hewers.

mates were killed in a similar accident but this is the only way the job could be done. I always remember the Bosses at the Colliery were more concerned with regard to the pony than the young lad. Horses cost £40 or £50 lads could easily be replaced. In 1941 the family left 'Witton Park'. And moved to 'Howden le Wear'. Mothers home village; the old man was still using his bicycle to travel to the 'Hole in the Wall Colliery' at Crook so this meant that it was a little closer for him.

The new house did not have a leaky roof, this was at Plantation Terrace. Neither did it have rising damp and the windows and doors fitted lovely. There was still only an outside toilet, no bath or hot water but to our joy it had electricity. Gordon and I had a little further to go to work but you can't have everything. These days work in the pits was plentiful and I felt ready for a change. I left and went to 'Steel House Colliery' at Crook. It happened to be a bad decision the ponies were still awkward, conditions still as wet. There was another big change at Steel House they worked shifts. Night shift and fore shift. 1.45am. to 9.45am. and 1.45 to 7.45am. The lads of my age should not be on this shift work and I pointed this out to the Gaffer. I was told *"don't you know there is a war on"* and told to get off my backside and make sure that I get to work by 1.45AM. The Gaffer had a way with words. At this time coal mines regulations said that (*'Pit ponies must have 20 minute feeding period during the shift'*, under this same act there was no provision for men or even boys) In a lot of ways ponies were more considered than men but to be fair it was very rare that the ponies got their meal period that was granted by law. Who's to know anyway; this pit as well as being wet was over run by rats. One Putter had died with 'Weils Disease', caused by water being infected by rat's urine. This infected an open cut in his leg. Another driver at a neighbouring Colliery was killed with the same disease. After about eighteen month's I returned to my first pit, which was 'Marshal Green'. My employment this time was 'Galloway Putting'. This was a little harder than driving but the pay was better at 30-35 shilling a week. After a few month's of this I was again on my travels as it shows over this period an experienced miner could get work any-where.

I began work at the 'Hole in the Wall', colliery where dad was employed; this time it was putting without a pony. This was absolute slavery; it must have been without hesitation the hardest work on earth. The roadways were no more than tub height so with a little *'Geological movement'*, the tubs were scrubbing the top and sides. It had another problem that was because it was low our backs caught onto the roof. All putters working this area had a line of scabs on their backs. They were called buttons. On occasions the tops of the scabs were knocked off and very painful to say the least. And we vent our pain by uttering close to the

THE TRADES UNION CONGRESS

Postal Courses Service Certificate

...................................Kenneth Robinson......................................*of the*

Nat. Assoc. of Colliery Overmen, Deputies & Shotfirers

has satisfactorily completed a course on

...................................Industrial Negotiations......................................

DATE....22.11.66.... B.G.C. CERTIFICATE NO....147727....

TUC General Secretary: George Woodcock CBE
Congress House, Great Russell Street, London WC1

THE TRADES UNION CONGRESS

Postal Courses Service Certificate

...................................Kenneth Robinson......................................*of the*

Nat. Assoc. of Colliery Overmen, Deputies & Shotfirers

has satisfactorily completed a course on

...................................Secretaryship......................................

DATE....13.4.66.... B.G. CERTIFICATE NO....144989....

TUC General Secretary: George Woodcock CBE
Congress House, Great Russell Street, London WC1

Ken had no intention of working on the coal face all of his life and he set about getting qualified to better himself; especially as the kids grew up

Above Ken with trophies won with the Dog; Ken was a Deputy and a member of NACODS Union below left taken in 1938 in the background the Robinson's home. Ken with brother Ronnie helping with the Milk. Right Mr. Walter Blackett the only Blacksmith in Witton Park. Worked from his shed near Kelly's Eye; now Royal Hotel; Ken was friendly with Walter:

bone words. The pay for hand putting was 8/- a score & 3p a score for each extra 20 yards. Tubs when empty weighed three hundred weights holding seven hundred weights so in total this was half a ton. The work was completed in six shifts each week, one-week days then night shift. After a considerable time on this work I started 'Windy Pick Hewing'. The price of this work was 1/11d. each ton; 18 shilling each yard for stonework. You had to pay for your own explosive, shovel, pick, also the sharpening of the same. One would think there was a fortune to make.

In 1943 the Bevan boys system came into being, due to the shortage of miners who at the time were fighting for their Countries. These lads were conscripted into the Pits they did not have any choice but to go. A Hostel was built near Crook; most of the lads in the Hostel were from areas around London and the South East of England. They did not have a clue about mining and what to expect, when they finally did find out it shocked them. Language was a further hurdle they did not have a clue what we were talking about. One told Ken that for the first three months the F. word was the only word he recognised. The majority of them its sad to say were totally useless; lads of 18-19 were completing the work of a fourteen year old.

The pits were Nationalised in 1947 a dream come true '*So we thought*'. The work was just as hard; conditions had not improved, '*Pay still as poor*'. The same bastards in charge, some dream. Family History in our family repeated itself; my Grandfather on mam's side was injured at work at 'North Bitchburn' and died shortly after. Now mam's brother Walter was injured at the 'Hole In the Wall', Colliery and he had a severe back injury. Some months later following a heavy snowfall he was walking down the street on Crutches when a heavy tanker came towards him. Walter got into a heap of snow, which had been pushed to the side by the snowplough. At this time Walter was a little unsteady on his legs and when the tanker was level with him he slipped under its wheels and the giant tanker ran over him he died a few days later. Walters Trade Union activities prevented him from working from 1926 to 1938.

After a while I felt that I should use my knowledge of mining to help where it would be most appreciated and I joined the 'Mining Rescue Service'. I was stationed at Ashington. I found that this was a great change from production work the hours were twenty-nine on, and nineteen hours off. It seemed long hours but we were allowed to sleep on the job and we had a weekend off every fourteen weeks. When any disasters occurred all time off was cancelled. At this time there were four Stations to cover the two Counties; Crook, Houghton le Spring, looked after Durham and Benwell Towers Ashington for Northumberland. This was a varied and interesting job. I had been courting my wife Lillian now for quite a while and we decided to marry. To this end I asked the Station Superintendent for some time off. He asked why I could not marry on my weekend off; he took a great deal of persuasion for him to allow me one day extra on top of my weekend. Lillian was a Stanhope girl from a decent Dale family. Her father was John Walton Forster. He was like most of his age in these days he had had a rough hard life. His family originated from further up the Dale they had been lead miners. Walt. had been wounded in the 1st. World War. He spent the remainder of his life in the Quarries in the Stanhope area. While working at the Quarry he was using a sledgehammer one-day and a piece came off the chisel and he lost an eye. This was not all, because of working outside in all weathers he got rheumatism in both hands and he had a job to move his fingers it brought it to mind that not only miners suffered because of hard times.

After our wedding there were no houses available in Ashington and shortly after we were offered a one back at Howden le Wear so it was back

Above an early Seaham rescue team in 1902; there had been so many death's in Northern Collieries from gas & other causes having a rescue team was essential to mining areas:

to the pits and this time to 'Holland Hall Colliery'. I commenced work again as a hand putter, this time the tubs were ten cwt. Instead of seven, the roof was a little higher so putters rarely caught their backs on the top. At this time a hewer got killed; he had served in the army during the Second World

War then later in Korea he returned home without a scratch only to loose his life very near to Home. It was not very long before I commenced coal hewing at Staindrop Field House Pit near West Auckland. Conditions were a little better here and there was two main seams one four feet the other 'The Brockwell' was six feet. The work was still as hard but the area was dry. After a short time I started hand filling and had an accident. There were three of us involved in a fall of stone and I was knocked about a little. These days sick pay was just not adequate and I was soon back with the shovel in my hand. Hand filling was a young mans game and a ten-yard stint each day was hard work. We were part of a team which at times was hilarious it was a laugh a minute. All young fit lads together. We got one shock when one day one of the lads Harry, stopped for a minute while walking out-bye. We had to catch the pit bus so we walked on. When the afternoon shift started they found Harry dead where we had left him. Later two Hewers were overcome by carbon Monoxide gas and died. By now we had two children Raymond born in 1953 and Ann in 1957 I began to think of security I studied and managed to get a Deputies certificate resuming my career with slave drivers of the worst kind. After a short while after receiving my ticket I went onto the staff. I worked hard in South West Durham in the following years mainly gaining experience; but it did not take many brains to note that coal production was slowing down and gradually demand for coal and its products were getting less and less. I began seriously thinking of contingency for the good of my wife and family even though it may mean leaving the area.

Deputy's responsibilities were varied and interesting, as well as production he was also responsible for safety. There had to be regular inspections infact every four hours. This was a staff position the lowest rung of the ladder. When off work because of sickness their wages were paid although overtime was not paid. Overtime was very frequent the rule included Christmas, New Year and Bank Holidays. At this time the NCB were closing more and more Collieries in the area; Staindrop Field House, then others followed quickly. I was forced to make the hardest decision in my life; I did not fancy any other industry as my experience was mainly in mining. I had noted that experienced miners were transferring to the Nottingham and Midland areas of the Country and I decided to leave Durham for pastures new.

Housing was now a big factor I had a young family to consider and I had two interviews for Nottingham & Yorkshire turning both positions down because of housing. Some expected you to live in lodgings without your family that I did not fancy. One day I saw a notice of miners required in Shropshire; housing was not a problem. I was not even aware that

Collieries existed in this area but the chance of housing was a big incentive and I accepted the challenge. The transfer situation was that the NCB collected your belongings on a Thursday then the family travelled down on the Friday to pick up the keys for the new house. We arrived in Donnington late afternoon and found the furniture wagon waiting at the door. We spent the weekend trying to put things in order. I was due to start work at 'Granville Colliery' on Monday. This had been the hardest decision of my life leaving my beloved Durham; mother was dangerously ill following a stroke and the day we left was the last we saw of her, as she died six month's later. Friend's neighbours and even surroundings were sadly missed. Worst thing of all was taking the kids away from their grandparents and also their friends and relations this decision had not been taken lightly and it certainly was not easy.

On the positive side I certainly did not want the pre-war period of mass unemployment effecting our lives I can remember similar happening years ago and I did not want this to happen to my family with no job and no future. Gordon and Ron had previously emigrated to Australia & it was quite natural for the old man to try and persuade us to stay in the North East he often said that as Pits go, factories would replace them 'Bullshit', I had been listening to that for years and as I write this forty two years after leaving Durham they still have not come to the Crook and Howden area sentiment does not fill bellies or for that matter put clothes on kid's backs So there was nothing left but to leave and seek work elsewhere. Dad always said give it a try and then come back home 'No Chance'. This was a one-way ticket; 'The boats burnt'. I remembered the advise he gave us after leaving school saying " From now on, you've got a pair of feet", "from now on stand on them" "and when the going gets rough the only person that you can rely on is yourself". The tough times had arrived for the family and myself.

Years ago when qualifying as a Deputy I remarked that another slave driver was in place. I cant have been all that bad as the lads took me out and bought me a drink before leaving home for Shropshire & Granville, the management never even bothered. The lads wished me 'Good Luck'. We finally left for Shropshire, there is a little saying that the grass is always greener on the other side of the hill, that may be so but the rocks are still has hard. When arriving at Donnington we were complete strangers, there were other families from Durham but none from our area. I reported to Granville on the Monday morning where I was still a Deputy; first impressions were not very good 'I thought that they were closing better pits in Durham to man pits like this. 'Like all of the world over', these miners here were all good decent lads just the same as home. The other thing that

I had came across was it was a Cosmopolitan Pit; the Manager was from Staffordshire, two under Managers one from South Wales the other was a Hungarian. There was an accumulation of workers from Durham, Scotland, North Wales, Lancashire, Jamaicans, Pakistanis, East Europeans, Poles, Ukrainians. They were certainly a mixed bunch of people. Employment was plentiful and a lot of the local lads did not stay long; I was still active in the Trade Union and the first NACODS meeting that I attended there was only six members present. The main reason for this was the meetings were held Saturday evenings at 7PM. Because of shift working most men anyway were not having much social life and Saturday nights was important to them; I proposed that we hold meetings on Sunday mornings. The Secretary agreed to ballot the members but he remarked if they wished to change the meeting to Sundays he would resign; being a Churchgoer. He actually did resign and the first Sunday morning there was attendance of about thirty members. I was elected Secretary and also appointed to the North Wales and Shropshire Executive Committee; I was also a member of the Trades Council, The Local Labour Party, Youth Employment committee, Disablement Advisory Committee, Apprentice Advisory Committee', the Local Technical College, and the Parish Council; I was certainly kept busy.

While I was employed as a deputy, there were three fatal accidents; and after a couple of years Granville Colliery became fully mechanised. This did not alter things in the pit a great deal but work was not as hard; the noise was far greater and the dust was increased as the coal production became faster. Overtime working increased and there was two seams to cover, the Top Coal, was four feet and the Main Coal was six feet, New Mine five foot on mechanisation and the Top Seam was closed. Most of the mined coal went to the Local Power Station at Iron Bridge. A few years after Nationalisation a Training Scheme was introduced. As I recall it was the best thing the NCB ever did. Lads were now leaving school until they were sixteen and they were not thrown into the deep end; like myself and thousands more. After four years as a Deputy at Granville; I was appointed as 'Training Officer'. Now I could make sure that the lads were fairly treated & cared for and were given proper training for individual jobs the youngest being as stated around sixteen.

Because of the improved standards, better housing a different type of miner was coming forward the lads seemed bigger than we were at the same age. As Granville was the last Pit in Shropshire it came under the Cannock area. Which was twenty miles away. As Training Officer I was responsible for the selection, recruitment and training of apprentices. Another responsibility was for adult miners who had transferred from other areas. At this time Granville employed about 1200 men so part of my job was the actual allocation of housing working hand in hand with local Councils. We also had a great deal of visitors; when we moved to Dunnington there were four working pits, now three had closed and all of the visitors visited Granville. These were a wide variety, school children, mature students, civil engineers, and soldiers from the local barracks, factory workers, young farmers clubs, and even local politicians. The latter mainly at Election times we even got visits from the local youth detention centre 'Borstal'. Another different aspect of the job.

We were even able to do something for the local retired miners; nothing in the past had ever been achieved for them so now it was up to us to arrange something. The locals had not previously thought of it and when it was suggested there was a great deal of interest and effort. Over the years I had been able to be aware when trouble was looming in the Industry and this was one of these occasions. Due to low wages and conditions a General Strike finally commenced in 1972. Local strikes were pretty common in the Industry and I had been involved in a few, but it was with mixed feelings when the lads went on strike this time. I had sad memories of the 1926 strike when we were starved back to work and union activists blacklisted for fighting passionately for their rights. This time with good organisation and leadership we won, gaining some improvement in pay with some conditions still to be improved. Having been victories once a further strike was called for 1974 and this again the miners won. Little did we know that the this would never happen again; the NUM would never be victories again and there would be a gentle spiral of humiliating defeats triggered by a Conservative Government, as Atomic Power Stations gradually took over the role of coal, our great natural product which we had depended on for wealth and prosperity for years.

All good things come to an end, as stated earlier Granville was not the pit they told us about at the interview, many problems were coming to a head and it was a very gassy pit. There was a Methane drainage system in operation, and the gas was piped to the local Gas Works but for what ever reason they no longer needed it; the drainage still had to be done but now they just released it into the air 'earning nothing'! Due to this and Geological and Ventilation problems in the Granville area, the pit found itself in trouble. The NCB asked me to again transfer to the Cannock area; they must of thought we were gypsies. Raymond was at the local Grammar school and Ann at the Secondary Modern school so like any parent would, I thought 'no chance'. So what on earth do I do now? I began looking round for work in a similar position and found again my luck was in. Local Authorities were looking for 'Experienced Safety Officers', this was brought about by a new act coming into force 'The Health & Safety Welfare Act of 1974'. This was unnerving some Companies; it also meant a lot of changes in the NCB. 'Lord Robens' (*not many miners respected him*) was appointed to Chair the Commission and thus implement this act. Most of the act was actually based on the NCB set-up. This enabled a few Overmen, Deputies etc. to leave mining and go into other industries. After thirty-six years in this amazing industry my employment was about to come to an end and I wish to make a few observations.

❖   **1/**   History proves throughout my lifetime miners have been badly treated and abused. Coal owners backed up by the establishment, Police, Courts, has no doubt about it treated them worse than animals. If a person these days greeted a dog similar to the Coal owners including the NCB. They would be held to task.

❖   **2/**   For centuries the miners had dreamed of Nationalisation as a means of fairness. When it arrived in 1947 it was greeted with joy. In reality it was a let down; the same gaffers were still in charge and the old coal owners received massive amounts of compensation for useless pits that had been allowed to run down because of lack of investment. Previous Governments had held the price of coal stable, thus enabling the manufacturing industries costs to a minimum. The easiest way to keep the price of coal down was to keep the wage of the miners low as well as conditions and it was carried out to the letter.

It was strange that even now miners still had their own tools to pay for, this together with explosives and protective clothing. The media made great capital on just how inefficient the industry was, having to pay out compensation to run down pits. The industry had a millstone around itself from the start. Coal owners should most certainly have received nothing or proved their compensation. Cash was misappropriated; people received money that they were not due to. Years later in the serious 'Foot and Mouth', period that nearly brought the Country to its knees the same thing happened although not as great. The Government in a lot of cases paid compensation that was paid erroneously. The Coal owners had extracted enough blood and sweat deaths and suffering from the Miners even though they no longer owned them.

What benefits we did get, they were hard fought for, and also helped other industries, the start of the five day working week; but due to mechanisation more overtime had to be worked. The best thing in my opinion was the introduction of the 'Training scheme'. Everyone got the training and supervision that they were entitled. Annual holidays were another benefit; Committee's and Trade Union Officials were given time to carry out union business. Consultative committees in my opinion were just a waste of time. Decisions were made at area level, their, main object was canteens and catering prices. All other decisions were taken at area level as stated. Safety committee's never prevented any accidents; mainly, the agenda allowed the discussion on accident, loss of labour and the number of man-hours lost since the last meeting. History has proved that 99% of all accidents were due to incompetent Management and greedy owners. Some examples of this were 'New Hartley', due to a pump beam fracture, which fell down the shaft thus closing it; costing 204 lives, as the exits were the only shaft and exit. In 1913 Senghenydd explosion when 439 men and boys lost their lives. This was the greatest loss of life in the Industry. Very bad ventilation allowed a build up of Methane gas, which causes explosions; in 1923 Falkirk where forty lives were lost due to an inrush of water. There had been no pre-boring to prove or dis-prove the existence of water close by. Aberfan in 1956 the majority of the lives lost were children and it was very heart breaking; this brought it home to every family environment in the Country and I am afraid to say down to inefficiency on behalf of the Coal Board because of an insecure waste tip.

All disasters are an heart breaking experience for all of the families involved but this one was the most tragic; parents pondered on their own young and the horrible implications of this horrible disaster. Everyone knows where the blame lies on infrequent occasions, Managers have been fined paltry sums; but the coal owners were always exonerated. None have been charged with manslaughter or any other serious charge *'after all what's a miner or two'*. It was alleged that Lord Robens when the Aberfan pit heap had to be levelled and made safe, ensured some of the cost was taken from money raised from the Charity that had been raised for the good of families and friends of the children. It just proves and strengthened the point that every penny raised had to be fought for by the rank and file.

Having got a job in 1974 with a local authority as a Safety Officer it was with heavy heart that that I leave my beloved mining forever 'ever the optimist'. There is an old saying ' you can't beat an old dog for a hard road'. Well I think I have travelled that road and had loads of laughs & Pleasure & pain along the way. The other old saying is that you can't teach an old dog new tricks, now's the time to find out. When starting this new job I was again fortunate as I was the first one in the local Authority to hold it, no one else had a clue about Health & Safety; this allowed me to set up my own system without the slightest interference. The system must have worked well because when the officer took over, after I retired, he continued with the same system. The work was strange to me being in the fresh air every day; travelling around building sites etc. The new town of Telford was in its early stages and new contracts were being undertaken by the Newtown

Development Corporation. The Local Authority, which was part of the New Town, was expanding and many National Companies such as McAlpines, J.H. Pearce, McPhillips, Fairclough's, and many more were tendering for work. High rise flats, office blocks, factories, houses, drains & sewers to mention just a few of the development going on.

I spent a great deal of my time going up & down scaffolding, in and out of drains & sewers, 'I was having a great time'. In 1986 the Authority was starting to offer early retirement and I was asked if I would like to accept. The Personnel Officer gave me a strange look when I informed him that I had been retired since 1974. I was always grateful to the Authority for letting me have the job; this enabled me to stay in employment until I was 65. This was a total of 51 years in total; never ever out of work. My greatest fear had always been unemployment; seeing so much of it as a youngster. The thing that I was grateful for was my health, other than accidents, being knocked about in the fall, a broken knee, fingers on one hand grafted, finger end on the other hand amputated, my health has been very good and I have lost very little work.

Now that dads dead, my oldest brother Gordon also dead, when Ron retired from mining in Australia our family link was broken. All other relations are either dead or retired. My son Raymond is the only male member for about five generations who has not been involved in mining and of this I am very pleased. As I look back life certainly has not been easy; having said that, I would not have changed it for the world. I have met a lot of good men along the way, some brilliant characters most with wonderful sense of humour and we certainly needed it in mining. Miners are unique and I am proud of being part of it. Even when I worked for the Authority, 'Although I enjoyed it', I still thought of myself as a 'Geordie Miner' who through circumstances was working elsewhere. I sometimes wonder did I leave the Industry or did it leave me. In 1974 the Mining Industry and I had been physically parted and certainly not mentally

The Great strike of 1972-74

This strike was all about pay, Robens forced these strikes upon us and when Gormley was leader of the NUM. The miner's wages slipped in the Industrial wage league beyond proportion. Some years the men received as little as 5/- another year nothing. It seemed to me that any Union Official who gets a knighthood after retirement was for service to the establishment and certainly not to his members. It was further noted in reports that he was betraying the lads during the 1974-75 strikes. The 1974-75 strike was forced onto the NUM. By an evil Tory Government who were after revenge after the union brought down the 'Heath Government'. It was later disclosed that they had spent millions of pounds preparing for this strike. The NUM. had to take some kind of action to try and avoid Pit closures. It was proved that the majority of Nottingham Miners were scum; this did not come as a surprise as they again black legged in the 1926 strike and formed a breakaway union 'The Spencer Union'. The only pleasure that I got when the strike was over was that the Government closed the Notts. Pits as well. The greatest hurt & shame I have ever felt in my life was during this strike the NACODS the Deputies union of which for several years I had taken an active part and proud to have been an official betrayed the lads. The union held a ballot and the result was a large majority in favour of strike action. Peter McNesstrey their leader and his executive committee held a meeting with the NCB. Then refused to bring the members out, even though it was already voted for; 'talk about 30 pieces of silver'. To shame me more was the fact that McNesstray was from Durham, actually from 'Little Moscow', Chopwell of all places. Even now as I go through my memories the shame is still with me. I certainly think that if he and his members had voted at this

time to strike there is every chance that the NUM. would have won the battle, as without deputies the blacklegs could not have produced the coal.

After fighting for twelve long months against the establishment, The Courts, Lying scheming and sometimes brutal National Police Force, Media that was not prepared, to do anything against the Government, the lads were sadly defeated and de-moralised. This time they did not get all of the public sympathy they should have got; because of certain stories appearing in the press that were later proved lies. It saddens me to see what happened at this time to a proud people and a great Industry. Today there is only about ten pits left in the Country and they are sadly back in private hands. I never thought I would live to see this happen. Some people have asked me if Mining was so rough and hard why did lads enter the Industry. I always explain until the war many lads were forced into the pits; they and

their families lived in tied cottages, houses owned by the Collieries; if the son never started at the pit the families mother and father stood a chance of loosing their home. No job, no house, no pay not a great lot of choice. That's the main reason why young men turned to the forces as an alternative even at the time of war. Myself, I went to the pits by choice I preferred to be in the Industry. Gaffers, although it went against the grain did not want to be seen going against the Government and 'War Effort'. I have tried to outline some of the hardships shared by miners but Miners wives also suffered tremendously and had a hard lives. My mother as a typical example of the conditions, I have already said what the houses were like until the mid fifties woman had no labour saving devices, no electric, or gas cookers, washing machines, vacuum cleaners electric kettles or Irons, no fitted carpets etc. My mother had to do all of the cooking, baking and boil water on an open coal fire with a large oven on the side. The fire never went out. It must have been a terrible backbreaking and hazardous job especially during the summer weather this would make the heat unbearable. It was always washing day Monday's. pan's were again needed on the fire to boil the water. Clothes prior to washing were placed in a large tub and beaten with a poss stick, put through a big hand mangle. If the weather was dry enough then the clothes were put out to dry; if the weather was wet they were hung inside of the house. The meals all had to be cooked; water for bathing all to heat. Tuesday was ironing day, no electric Iron the old flat iron was heated on the fire. Mother always baked bread twice a week; the old cast iron fireplace also needed black leading and polished Fridays. To add to mothers work-load sometimes dad, Gordon and I worked different shifts making three different meal times. Due to working conditions while working food consumption was limited so at the end of the shift we were all ready for a hot meal. Mother could be cooking 9.30 am. 3.30 am. and midnight. In addition because we worked in wet conditions our entire pit clothes had to be washed and dried ready for the following day. The clothes also had to be patched and stitched, socks darned. She also did a lot of knitting, socks, jumpers infact anything to keep the cold weather out, a typical North East wife and mother was hard to come by. Beds had to be turned out shopping sorted out, decoration of the house completed, most evenings we all helped to cut old clothes for making mats, especially in the winter months.

The only relaxation mother got was Sunday evenings attending the Methodist Chapel. All of the family attended the Chapel and I still remember receiving a prize for attending regular and reciting a piece at the Anniversary. The old man never much attended Chapel except at the Anniversary Sunday; although there was three pubs on Black Road, The Royal, Rose & Crown and the Puddlers Arms Dad did not drink at all. Added to everything else these days it was a worrying experience trying to run a home on little money. Three of us were working regular and at this time Ron was at school later joining the Navy. Mam was only sixty-three years old when she died of a stroke; this happened just as Dad was retiring. I felt sure that her death was due to being permanently fatigued. The saddest thing of all was, we had all left home and dad was just retiring so for once in her life things would have been a lot easier. Mam was the type of woman that was typical of North Country woman in general. Men were injured and killed because of mining and their woman folk died of stress related problems during the same period. The period of the 26 strike, the Depression in the 30s this was a terrible hard period in our lives. The miners were locked out for six long months, there were three young children at home; I was six months old, Gordon 18 months, and Olive 3 ½.years old; five mouth's to feed and no money. We had to depend on Soup Kitchens and Charity from some of the Business people.

My parents never forgot our local Milkman, 'Mr. Billy Milner', without being asked he left a pint of milk each day; later after the strike my parents repaid him. Dad always said that most Business people were very supportive to the Miners cause, but there were others who did not care. One or two little things added to our problems over this period as I mentioned the coal fire was all important in our lives and there was one day mam asked dad to open the window to allow some fresh air into the room.Dad pulled up the window but because the cord had rotted the window

dropped sharply onto his hands trapping them. Gordon and I had to quickly lift the window from his hands. Dad's hands were badly bruised and he had to go to Doctor Camas to get them dressed. Dad was back to work the following day, no work no money; this happened in 1938 while living at Black Road.

Despite the hardships and the Miners many obstacles we all struggled through, on occasions I wonder how! But we got through. Many household names lived in the district some becoming M.Ps; others joined the ranks of Professional sportsmen, some boxers who became 'World Champions', some International Footballers and Rugby players. Brian Fletcher, (*Grand National winning jockey*), *Tom McGuinnes the famous artist and* The fighting Bradfords hailed from Witton Park, James, Roland, George and Thomas. These were the most decorated family in the First World War. George and Roland won 'Victoria Crosses, James awarded the 'Military Cross and Thomas won the Destinguished Service Order and was later Knighted. The Colliery brass bands were magnificent together with Male voice choirs'. There were many class breeders of Racing Pigeons and Whippets. It was all wonderful and typical of the area. Like most Northern people I have always been into the past times of the area for a while I enjoyed Whippet Racing. At present I live happily with my wife Lillian, we have a Bedlington terrier, and it gives me great pleasure to take it for a walk. I also occasionally do a little gardening and I have an Avery with a few exotic and colourful birds that give Lillian and myself much happiness.

I also took the advice given by my old Head Master in that reading is the best thing in the world; I now have a fine collection of books. These are mainly made up of Mining and general History of my beloved North East, Coal, Lead, and Railways. I have only been to one football match in my life and that was when I was sixteen years old. I am actually very interested in Boxing; when just eleven years old dad got us out of bed to listen to the Tommy Farr v Joe Louis fight, my other great love is collecting artifacts & memorabilia from the Mining period such as Lamps, Plates, Photograph's, Print's. Lillian always says that if I continue collecting we will need a bigger house.

Every year we travel to 'Durham Miners Gala'. I never ever miss this event. When dad and my sister Olive was a alive I returned home about four times a year but now sadly we return just for the Gala although it remains a big day in our lives. A matter of a few years ago after the Pit Closures the event was badly attended but now every year it gets better and better, more bands, Banners and Mining folk are again

attending to mark the event as an important day in the lives of miners some not with us any more but still remembered with pride. It is now forty-two years since we left Durham for Shropshire; I still refer to it as home. While living here we have been very lucky and the ball has always bounced right for us. All of the family have done well. I always had work and I have made many friends. My thoughts were always with the Durham people and Often wondered what kind of life I would have had if I remained in the Durham area, my mother and all of her family were strong Methodists, although not being a Church man myself I respected those who were. I have always in life been a 'Socialist', may I add not the Blair type.

I always try to help anyone wherever possible believing that an ounce of help is worth more than pity. When I think it was the pits that brought my family north and the lack of them the reason why we left. On reflection I did not think my family would ever leave the Durham area; Gordon and Ron emigrated to Australia, Gordon is now dead and Ron's wife is a Filipino. My son Raymond who is now in America gained a Degree in 'Graphic Art & Design', Raymond worked for many years in the Fire Service but twenty years ago he travelled to, & settled in America; he is head of the European History Department of a Los Angelus High School at present and enjoys his life in the States. He is married to a lovely Chinese girl. 'The World must be small as well as being funny', all I have in Durham are two cousins and they are all in there 80s. It's sad to think that after them our family will be none existent in my beloved Durham. I am now 79 years old and still enjoying a good healthy life. If I last as long as Gordon I have another eleven years to live. I have enjoyed penning this small record of my life as a miner at Durham while it brought me much pain it also brought me much happiness.

Note:
Kens search for fairness and good working practices rubbed off on his daughter & Partner who are full time Union Representatives with the GMB Union. Ann Rixom is a full time organiser with the GMB. Trade Union. An article appeared in Issue 7, winter 'Centre Point', magazine. A member wrote thanking her for her brilliant representation in his case against his Employers. This could easily have effected his employment and would also have effected his general health. Ann skilfully guided him through the crisis, and he & his wife were very grateful.

THE INDESPENSABLE MAN

Some Time when you're feeling important,
Some time when you're Egos in Bloom,
Some time when you take it for granted,
You're the best-qualified man in the room,

Some time when you feel that you're going,
Would leave an infallible hole,
Just follow these simple instructions,
And see how they humble your soul,

Take a bucket and fill it with water,
Put your hands in it up to your wrists,
Pull them out and the hole which remains,
Is the measure of how you are missed?

You may splash all you like when you enter,
You may stir up the water galore,
But stop and you'll find in a minute,
That it looks just the same as before,

The Moral of this is quite simple,
Do just the best that you can,
Be proud of yourself and remember,
There is no indispensable man.

Away from the cold and drab Colliery areas was the wonderful views of Hamsterley:

Bernard McCormick worked at Bowburn Colliery after leaving Cornforth Lane School. After five years he left the pits and completed his National Service with the 13/18 Royal Hussars, in Malaya during the Emergency where he saw active service. After Being demobbed he married, his wife Eileen, then Worked twenty years in Engineering. Later he ran a successful designer Clothing Business. Bernie, now retired writes extensively on Family and Local History. He has written four books on Northern and Scottish characters in the Northern and Scottish Folk series, and has researched, written and edited his family history, which includes four families. Bernard has also written books on North East mining, including 'Troubled Collieries', which was a great success especially in the North East; and which he is reprinting again, & includes four more Collieries and an extra fifty pages. Bernard is researching the Coulson's & Robson's on his mother's side, Jane Fletcher Coulson, who were all Colliery owners & shaft sinkers.

Bernie has written and published a pictorial group of books on Coxhoe and district where he was born. A book not yet published is 'The Pease Dynasty', which traces the early beginnings of the S&D Railway at Darlington and the people involved in establishing this brilliant time in North East History.

In 2003 Bernard signed a Contract with 'Business Education Publishers Limited', *(Leighton),* to produce 'Northern Folk 1 & 2 as one volume of 24 stories of Northern Characters, the people who made the area what it is today. It even includes a greatly loved poetess Elizabeth Browning and Painter Lowry. This book will be able to be bought from Leighton Web site on WWW.bepl.com or myself: